The Scentual Way to Success

An Aromatherapy Experience for Business and Life

by

Jennifer Jefferies ND

Dedication

To my parents for enabling me to enter this world
in the first place.
And
To my partner Toni, who helps make my world
a more pleasurable place to live.

THE SCENTUAL WAY TO SUCCESS
An Aromatherapy Experience for Business and Life

Published by
Living Energy Natural Therapies
Shop 1, Shaws Arcade
Flinders Street Mall
Townsville, Queensland 4810
Australia
Phone 61 7 4721 3124
ISBN 0-646-37739-6

Disclaimer

The information contained in this book is not intended as medical advice, but as general information only. The author/publisher cannot accept responsibility for any mishap resulting from the use of essential oils, or other therapeutic methods described in this book. My advice to the reader is to realise you are an individual, and as such, I recommend you consult a professional Aromatherapist or health care professional if treatment or advice is required.

Printed in Australia by Watson Ferguson and Co, Brisbane.
Typesetting by Norste Enterprises, Townsville.
Illustrations by Karen Lauder, Townsville.

Acknowledgements

Where to start. Take me back to anywhere in my past and I can honestly say that I never imagined my life would take the direction it has. I love my life and the beautiful people in it. I treasure, and I am eternally grateful for, the friendships I have with the men and, in particular, the women in my life. Exquisite beings that have inspired me to be the woman I am today. From my life teachers: my family, clients and friends, to the "ratbags" I have truly "lived" with along the journey. We are all an accumulation of many life experiences. So thank you to those who have been part of my experience, and to those who helped guide me on my chosen path.

A special thank you to my dear friend, Ms Robbi Zeck, my Aromatic Kinesiology teacher who introduced me to the emotional talents of the essential oils. Robbi's work, and my experiences working with her teachings, inspired me to write this book. And to Salvatore Battaglia, my Aromatherapy teacher and mentor for originally lighting my passion for studying Aromatherapy. To Ms Karen Lauder, thank you for the divine and "interesting" illustrations, and for your intriguing sense of humor that went with them.

The most special thank you, however, goes to my life partner and partner in life and business, Ms Toni Esser. A most beautiful woman, whose love I treasure. This book would not have happened if not for her patience and understanding. In that, I like to make changes in the world every single day. Being with Toni I am able to "live and not just exist".

About the Author

Jennifer Jefferies is a Naturopath and Aromatherapist with more than ten years experience as a practitioner and internationally accredited lecturer of natural therapies. Jennifer has personally travelled the road to ill health and business burnout and back. From being indoctrinated into the regimented work ethic of the regular army at 17, to exploring new directions in personal growth and development.

Jennifer now owns her own company and lectures internationally on "Steps to Success". She has made flexibility a part of her life, applying it as a principle for direction at work and at home. This is a principle that Jennifer believes is essential to achieving growth and success in life.

Jennifer inspires her readers to take responsibility for, and control over, their personal and business health. She writes generously, inviting readers to take home actual skills, tried and proven, that can be applied to everyday business and private life.

Jennifer draws on a wealth of diverse life experiences to fire up the imagination, to energise, and to motivate. Jennifer is an entertaining writer who stirs readers to:

"Stop existing and start living".

Meet Zelda

When I first asked friend and colleague Karen Lauder to illustrate my book, I had a vague idea of what I was after. I'd had the pleasure of viewing Karen's artwork in the past, and I knew that she would be able to duplicate what I was thinking. Karen did so beautifully, and so I would like to introduce you to Zelda.

Zelda has the vitally important task to help you to visualise the emotional properties of the essential oils, and to "hang out" in the book, generally.

Contents

How to use this book

I wrote this book primarily for people to have for a quick reference to the emotional benefits of the essential oils. These recipes and ideas can be useful in business and in personal life. It has been designed so that you can open it at any page and get something relevant to your life at that moment. You may open at a page and find an essential oil compatible with an emotion that you are, or have been, experiencing. You could then take the opportunity to use that oil or combination of oils to re-balance yourself.

I have also incorporated ideas, on what I see as the influences and causes of imbalance in people's lives. This comes from personal experience and through working with my clients. You may turn to a page where the topic may "push your buttons" emotionally, and from that you will derive whatever message or relevant information you require. Use the book as you wish. I have written it in simple language, and have strived to make it as user-friendly as possible. I hope you enjoy it, realise the benefits of essential oils and their subtle talents, and learn to start living again.

Introduction

I was first motivated to write *The Scentual Way to Success*, when I found for the lay person, there were no "easy to read" books on the emotional talents of essential oils. My second motivation was to share some of my life adventures and to offer insight to the what, why and how of my life's re-balancing and success using Aromatherapy.

Defining success: *"To reach a place in your life where you are satisfied with what you have, what you are doing, and with what you have achieved."*

That, point of satisfaction is going to be different for everybody. Because what is important to me will vary from what is important to you. The reality is there are so many paths that can be taken, and the path you choose will change as you grow. The path may have gone from being very rocky and exciting to very smooth and effortless at various times in your life. I wanted to share some of my thoughts and beliefs as to how I benefited from travelling my path. I have only travelled this particular path for the past 10 years, after being on a very different one for many years.

On my previous journey, I considered myself successful. I had all of the materialistic things: the right house, the career and relationship. But I felt empty inside. About this time, I had a car accident that left me with a few injuries that needed time to heal. Being an out-of-balance workaholic, I had no time to be ill and needed to be well straight away. I met some natural therapists when I checked into *Camp Eden* (a health retreat on the Gold Coast) to regain my health. During my stay, the practitioners helped re-establish my health to the best that it had been in my adult life. I was excited. For the first time in years I had regained my passion for life. I was living instead of just existing, and I realised that I had been given an exciting opportunity to make change in my life. So I did. I would never have dreamt that the roads I have taken would have led me to where I am now, and to the adventures that I have seen.

I believe that we are presented with opportunities and choices every minute of the day. The decisions we make are reflected in the life we

lead, and the satisfaction and success we achieve. After leaving the health retreat, I commenced studying natural therapies, I was curious and wanted to know how they could restore my health across all areas of my life, when conventional medicine could not. I wanted to unearth the how and why of everything, to learn more, and to share my learning with others. The desire is stronger even more so these days because in my clinic I see many people who are stagnating. I find that unfortunate, but I also believe that everyone can change the quality of their life if they want to and decide to do so. You just have to make a conscious decision and be determined. Stay focused on the positives and believe you can. The following information will give you some insight into what I see as the basic philosophy behind natural therapies, and is designed to stimulate a desire to re-balance all areas of your life.

The information on the essential oils comes from my training and experiences working with clients in the natural therapy modality called Aromatic Kinesiology. This is a system of healing that utilises the emotional talents of the essential oils. The goal is to re-balance the emotions and release negative patterns behind physical manifestations and stresses. This will enable you to prevent illness and imbalance in the first place.

Everyone thinks of the physical areas first, eating healthy, exercise etc, but we forget the emotional side most of the time. In my practice, I specialise in re-balancing all areas: body, mind and spirit. It is only then that we are truly in balance and able to be passionate about life.

This book focuses on recognising emotional imbalances, and ways to correct them. It also focuses on the emotional benefits of Aromatherapy Essential Oils, and the means by which to integrate them into your personal and business life, so that you, too, can regain that passion.

'Life is a daring adventure, or nothing.'
Helen Keller

Life's Like a Triangle

The following is a summary of ways to care for yourself and regain responsibility for your personal and business health. I explain the importance of working with the emotional benefits of the essential oils.

My passion in life is helping people regain responsibility for their own health on all levels. As an Aromatherapist and Naturopath, I see many people caught up in the same old cycles and patterns. At some time we need to recognise these patterns and change them, if we are to grow.

My explanation of how to identify the influences on illness is demonstrated using a triangle, which is used as a symbol for the exercise and is explained later in this chapter. Understanding the triangle allows you to take responsibility for your own health, because ultimately, you are the only one in control of your life. You can choose to react or respond consciously or subconsciously, positively or negatively to any situation in life. The way you respond will then determine the outcome, both physically and emotionally. This concept can push buttons, because when you truly understand it (and it is easy if you want to) you have regained responsibility for all areas of your life. Now this can be scary or exciting. You get to choose your own interpretation.

Fear and excitement are the same emotion, except that the first represents its negative side and the second, its positive side. You choose which to experience in your life. A large percentage of the population chooses to select the negative because it is easier in the short term. although this may eventually manifest some horrific disease or incident, they choose it because they do not have to accept responsibility for it. When you accept responsibility, you can no longer play the victim and gain attention that way. People play victim to get attention. They do not know how to ask for help, so they create physical or emotional problems to do it for them. I think it is much easier to just ask for the attention in the first place, rather than become stressed and manifest an illness. People do not always notice that you need extra attention. Remember, it is never too late to re-educate partners,

team members at work or friends, to be there for you when you need them. They are not mind readers, and may not pick up on your non-verbal signals.

Patterns are just patterns. It may sound simplistic, but we can change them if we choose. It is empowering to recognise some of the patterns in your life that are not working for you. Just recognising them is a start, for it is then that you can take steps to correct behaviours and change these patterns.

Life in Australia is still easy going and more personal compared with lifestyles in some countries, but we still feel isolated and reluctant to seek comfort from others. We are not meant to handle everything on our own. To prevent burnout, sometimes we need to ask for that extra assistance and nurturing from a partner, work colleague or friend. They like most of us, get stuck in their own world at different times, and may not notice that you need some help and/or attention. So just ask! I have more respect for people who realise that they need help and ask for it, than for those who choose to be the martyr and struggle.

An element of your past negative patterns could be that you beat up on yourself when you get caught out in performing a negative pattern. I tell my clients to give themselves a pat on the back and to reward themselves in some way instead of beating up. Identifying them is the only way we can correct negative patterns. Do not beat up on yourself, but be pleased and excited that you at least noticed. This will give you the courage to make a correction. When you first start being responsible in this way, you could catch yourself out every five minutes. I know, I have. This is okay.

Just start again, let it go, and keep moving forward. Otherwise, you hand over your power to that negative and reinforce it, instead of breaking it down. What you notice after a while, is that you have not caught yourself out, and are effectively correcting the behaviour or pattern. That's exciting. You generally need three weeks to seriously correct a habit and set a new pattern in place. It is worth the three weeks. And remember, just take it a day at a time if that's what you need.

Every now and then you may slip up, and again that's okay. Just let it go, focus on the positives and get going again. Through my own experience, and working with clients in my clinic, I know this works. You simply have to decide to do it, and then jump in feet first. If you keep waiting for the right time when there is no stress etc, you will never start, because it never comes. This is just a subconscious sabotage because the pattern has been useful in hiding and protecting us from fronting our emotions. It is not always easy at first, but the benefits are amazing.

Now the Triangle

The triangle is a way or system of explaining the elements involved in producing illness. We draw on the three points of the triangle, and when all three are running in the positive state, we stay well. Fit the three sides into a negative state, and we get sick. This helps to explain the holistic way that natural therapists look at life, and this is my explanation of it.

The three points of my equilateral triangle are as follows:

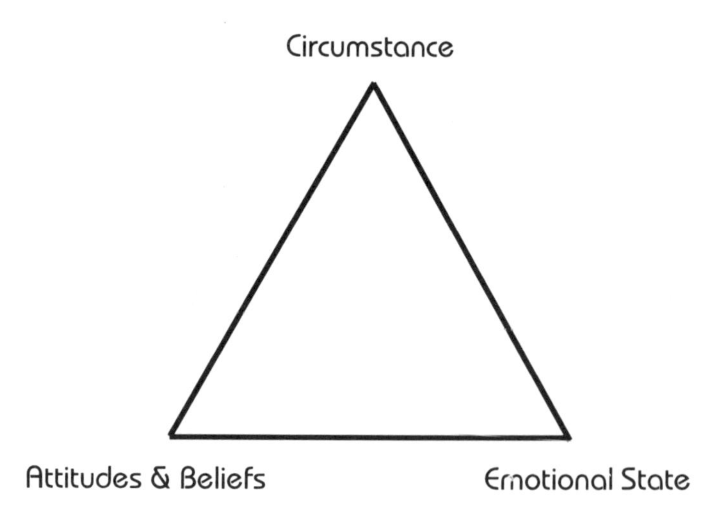

Attitudes and beliefs

This is the matter that we have ingested subconsciously over the years, creating our attitudes and our belief systems. These attitudes and beliefs hang around in the subconscious waiting to be used. Remember your mother telling you not to go outside in the cold weather without a singlet on, or you would catch a cold? Statements like these were projected onto us in our childhood and adult years—not just from parents, but from many others of significance in our environment. We took in the material consciously and subconsciously and it is now stored somewhere in our memory banks.

Nowadays, we don't pay it any conscious attention, but it is still there having an influence on how and why we do the things we do in life. The statements, manifested as a belief on some level, can come alive at any time and influence our physical and emotional health.

I believe they influence all areas of our lives. Have you ever heard yourself say something you have not thought of in years, yet remember hearing your parents say the same thing to you? Where did it come from? It fascinates me, the patterns we repeat throughout life. We do not consciously decide to do it, I know that as a child I heard myself saying I was not going to "be like that", or "act that way when I grow up." But before I knew it, I was repeating those behaviours. Then I started looking for, and noticing, these patterns. I started to catch myself out and correct these behaviours and attitudes that did not work for me.

A saying goes: "What you resist, persists" and this is relevant here. The more you try to *not* be like your parents, for instance, the more you become like them. Our attitudes and beliefs come from our experiences, consciously and subconsciously, in life. And if we focus on *not doing a particular thing*, our bodies only hear to do that thing. We give away so much of our power trying not to do it, that it gains the upper hand and wins. So the first thing to do is to recognise the pattern and then not empower it with any unnecessary energy or attention.

Emotional State

The second point of the triangle is that of your present emotional state. We are more susceptible to "catching" ailments when we are running stressed. To define stress, personally, I think that it is a catch word for life, and the way we choose to react or respond to what is happening. Again, we can call it negative or positive. It is simply how we look at it. If we refuse to listen to our bodies and keep pushing them beyond their limits something has to crack. If we do not stop and listen to our bodies, it will bestow an ailment upon us. This is to stop us and make us listen.

Have you ever heard people say they caught a cold or flu, just when they did not have time for it? Or, that they always catch "two colds a year", or "everyone at work is sick, I bet I catch it too"? It is almost as if they are subconsciously setting themselves up. I am sure they do not really want the cold, but on some level they like the attention that sick people attract. They feel sorry for those feeling unwell, and before long they are getting attention for the same reason.

In our home, my partner, Toni, and I joke about how we never get "sympathy and attention". If we get an ailment or hurt ourselves, we quiz each other as to what we were thinking at the time, and why it was manifested. We then work out on what level one needs to give the other more attention or what behaviour needs correcting. Some may think that sounds cute or over the top. But we know how our relationship and our health has improved by using this system. This can then cross over into all areas of life. You can choose to make the effort and reap the benefits.

Circumstance

The third point is that of circumstance. This is the event or happening that collided with you. Take the not wearing a singlet on a cold day scenario. The circumstance is the cold weather. You could be out playing golf and having a great time, but it may also be raining. You are not dressed warmly, but you are having such an

enjoyable, positive time that you do not have a chance of catching anything negative that day. On the other hand, you could be caught late after work and tired from your day at the office, when the car breaks down in cold and wet weather. You have the emotional "too hards", and you are running plenty of negative stress. Guaranteed, this is the time you will catch the cold.

With the triangle, consider what patterns or incidents you may be setting up for yourself without actually thinking about it. When you are struck down with an ailment, think about what is coming up or has just happened that could have caused enough stress to manifest, or exacerbate, an ailment. There are many books on this subject, and I have listed the details of a few of my favourites in the suggested reading list at the back of this book.

Self Talk

We have all heard of how keeping a positive mental attitude helps to keep us balanced. Using positive self talk, or keeping a positive mental attitude, is invaluable. Our self talk is that little voice that tells us from time to time that we are "not good enough", "it's too hard", or that we "cannot do" something. We are in control of our self talk, and yet so many people let it control them. Those little messages we give ourselves can create negative or positive belief systems, or attitudes, about ourselves. This is the root of so many major ailments. Certainly the circumstance point of the triangle is part of the equation in getting ill. But we literally feed it with our negative self talk.

Anyone and everyone can be positive and in control of their self talk and their lives, if the desire is there. So, if you are sick of feeling out of control, and down in the dumps, negative and depressed, deciding to do something about it is the biggest part of the journey.

But as previously mentioned, be aware of what you say and do, catching yourself off guard when you use negative self talk. Give yourself a pat on the back and be happy when you did catch yourself out. Your old pattern was *not* noticing and *not* correcting it. If you punish yourself with more negative self talk, you simply reinforce the negative. Instead, reinforce the positive and be happy that at least you noticed. It may be happening frequently at first, but that is okay. We are all individuals and we will handle things differently.

> 'Very little is needed to make a happy life. It is all within yourself, in your way of thinking.'
>
> *Marcus Aurelius*

It's Easy

My partner and I have a rule within our work and home environments, that we do not use negative words, and especially, double negatives. My pet hates are "no worries", "no problem", "no hassles" etc. When you ask someone for something and they say "no worries", their body actually hears the negative worry part. No and worries, for instance, are two very negative words tied together.

We already have enough stress in the world and any edges we can trim will help. Through my personal experience, using positives like "it's easy", as a substitute, works. These are not the only ones, but just listen to yourself. Notice how many negative words you use and how many times you use them. It is simply a habit that we have learned and it can be changed very easily, if the desire is there.

Some people may think, "how important is that?" When Toni and I first replaced "no worries" with "it's easy", reactions were visible on people's faces. The effect was instantly noticeable, and it set us apart as being positive and different from our business competition and friends.

It's easy is a positive response so simple and basic to be almost ridiculous. But our bodies hear what we say out loud and inwardly. Imagine if everything in your personal and business life was easy. What a pleasure work and life could be, and they *can* be, if you choose. It costs nothing to try, and you get to enjoy people's reactions!

> 'Let your inspiration feed others, and give them the juice to grow, and to glow.'
>
> *Sark*

If It's Hard To Do, All The More Reason To Do It

This is the rule by which I choose to live my life. If something is really hard to do or overcome—it may be a fear or just something unpleasant—we can choose to do it, to finish it, and move on. While we sustain that fear, we give away our power to it. Regain that power and just do it. Jump in feet first and stop procrastinating, then life will be more enjoyable. If it pushes your buttons a great deal, there is a special lesson to learn from doing or overcoming that obstacle. Push through. You may have to grit your teeth or hold your breath, but when you come out the other side, you will fly. You will feel empowered, and you will know you can do anything. Maybe you just need to break the problem into bite-size pieces. But at least make a start. If you keep waiting for the right time to conquer the problem—when everything is perfect—you could wait forever. So just do it, and **make now the right time.**

Learn to speak from your heart, and speak your truth. In this way you tie emotion with logic. This is not just fluffy, "hippie trippy" thinking, you will relate to all areas of your life better, and be more productive, when you are connected between reason and emotion. It is important to have your heart and head linked, although in the 1980s, many of us were not connected to anything emotional, and we now know the consequences of that folly for business.

It is a strength to have your heart and head connected. Being in touch with your feelings does not make you weak, but aids you in connecting more effectively with those around you. Be the one strong enough to recognise and make positive changes in your personal and business life. Step outside the box, and complete the hard tasks first.

'What would you attempt to do if you knew you could not fail?'

Robert Schuller

Why We Sabotage

As much as we "whinge" when things are not running to our expectations, on some level it seems easier to do this and be unhappy, than to do something about it. We carry around our negative beliefs subconsciously, not planning to let them emerge, but they have been around for so long they usually remain. Our negative patterns and beliefs are comfortable where they are, and the effort it sometimes takes to identify them is enormous. Once identified, though, we have to do something about them. Often people choose to leave them alone and put up with the consequences.

It may be the old habit of eating to nurture yourself, instead of asking for the emotional attention that you really crave. For instance, so many relationships are "full on" these days, as is life in general, but when do you schedule time for "play"? The trick is to just start. The right time rarely comes, and all the while you are getting emotionally lower and lower, digging a pit for yourself to hide in. You can be the most assertive person externally, showing the world a persona of success. Strong and confident on the outside, yet emotionally low and insecure on the inside. Does this affect you? You may think you have it all in check, nicely packed away where you can control it. But when you least need them, those insecurities raise their heads.

I believe that we sabotage ourselves because it is easier than facing our emotional challenges. It is okay to be human and want to *not* be unhappy. But by trying *not* to be unhappy, we can end up artificially happy because we have suppressed something that we feel is unpleasant to face.

Time for change. You have to start sometime, and I have found working with Aromatherapy essential oils one of the most pleasant ways to release fears, and return to a place of real happiness.

Start right now. Think of something that you find uncomfortable that keeps coming up and holding you back. It could be simply sneaking that extra piece of unhealthy take-away food or drink. This is a subconscious sabotage on your health, stopping you from looking feeling and being your best. What is the payoff for that food you put into your mouth? Punishing yourself for the next week. Remember, it is not what you do 10 per cent of the time, but what you do 90 percent of the time, that matters. So concentrate on being positive in all areas of your life: emotionally, nutritionally, physically, spiritually, and indeed every area.

Emotional Manifestations
at home and at work

There have been many books written on the subject of how, what and why, people manifest ailments in their bodies or acquire imbalance in their business etc. Our physical and emotional health is reflected in our workplace and our environment. Have you had the experience of locking the keys in the car, or doing all of those "Monday-itis" things? Perhaps you just do not want to face what is going on at work today.

I once heard Ita Buttrose, (Australian Journalist/Editor "Queen") say: "If you are not doing what you would want to be doing if you were going to die in six months, get out of it." I totally agree with this statement. If you are not doing what you want, you are taxing your physical, emotional and spiritual health. It may reflect in your home life or at work. So change it now, because you are not doing yourself and your friends, partners, or associates any good being there. So many people wait until they hit rock bottom to make changes—I did, many years ago. I know now that life would have been much easier if I had taken responsibility much earlier, but I believe I was not meant to at that time. We all have our own time. Just leave yourself open to the possibility and start integrating changes as you can, and embrace the excitement, opportunities, and the positive changes it brings.

One change I made concerned allergies. I always thought that I was allergic to lots of things, from cats and pollen to life as a whole. I always got the full-on allergic attack, with runny nose, itchy eyes, and the rest. When I had it, I just wanted to stay in bed all day. When I first started looking at my life differently, this was one of the first imbalances I wanted to fix. So I looked for a pattern. Using the triangle, the

attitudes and beliefs part of the triangle was in place—I honestly believed that I was allergic to everything! The circumstance was in place—there would be a cat or some pollen around. But the part I had not thought of in the past was the emotions I was experiencing at the time.

What I found was that the only times I manifested a heavy hayfever attack was when I had to do something I did not want to do, or when I had to go somewhere I did not want to go. Or, I was emotionally overtired and basically, just wanted to stay in bed. Literally, something or someone was "getting up my nose". Of course I did not consciously seek all of those symptoms. But sure enough, I did get them and I had the perfect excuse to play "poor me" and escape doing what I did not want to do in the first place.

To break the pattern, the first thing I did was recognise the trigger, that it was just a pattern that could be changed. I then noticed whenever I presented with a symptom of hayfever, I would ask myself what had happened in the previous hours, and/or, what was approaching in the next day or so. Generally, as soon as I identified the emotion involved the hayfever started to settle. Previously, it would carry on for days, and yes, I received plenty of sympathy and attention too.

Now I deal with the emotion as it arises. My hayfever settles, and I am quickly symptom free, without medication. If someone gets "up my nose" I say something and deal with it. If I do not want to do something, I choose how I am to handle it, for example, by changing my perception as to why it would be stressful to me. I handle it in my way and in my time. I accept responsibility for it, and get on with it. I still get snotty noses occasionally, but the people in my life know not to give me attention.

We all have the "stress" areas of our bodies. That place where, whenever we are stressed, we generally manifest a symptom. Can you imagine how great it feels to be in control and not let the symptoms control you? I am very passionate about this, because I know how control has changed my life, and it can change yours too, if you choose.

Remember, if you ignore what is not working and you do not fix it, it will follow you. Have you ever found that after leaving a relationship, your next partner has similar qualities? He or she has interesting (annoying) habits just like the last partner, mind, you only notice these after you settle down and move from the lust to the love stage of the relationship. Or, have you changed jobs because you could not get on with the boss or your co-workers, and found that the new job presents similar problems after you have settled in? Why are you attracting these problems? I call them learning experiences, because you are in that environment and with those people to learn something. Only you know what it is, and perhaps you need to access help from a practitioner to realise the lesson to be learnt. Otherwise you may find yourself constantly changing jobs and relationships, and still never finding happiness. Do it now, start looking and seeing the answers. They are there, it is just that you have been used to playing "poor me" and enjoying the attention that behaviour reaps.

'Discontented minds and fevers of the body are not to be cured, by changing beds or businesses.'

Benjamin Franklin

Do What You Want To Do, Be What You Want To Be. NOW

Believe in your dreams, that is the "secret" to life. For dreams to be manifest you have to put them "out there," and start to live them now. To simplify it, how many time have you thought "I have to catch up with Mary Smith", and surprise, Mary rings you or you see Mary down the street. It is as if you put your energy and thoughts out there, and they found the person concerned. And how often have you attracted something negative by thinking things like "I don't want to see that person" or, "I don't want to catch that cold that's going around"? And, sure enough, the negative energy manifests the undesired outcome. You run into that person you are trying to avoid, or you catch the cold. So start focusing your energy on positive self talk and affirmations. We have all heard of using affirmations: positive self talk and a positive attitude, and we have to start somewhere, so put only positives out there.

If you want a promotion at work, start *being* the person with the promotion. Don't wait. Do what you want to do and be what you want to be, *now*. Waiting could be fatal. We do not have a crystal ball to see everything that is around the corner, so take charge and make it happen. I recall a saying once that read:

'Don't wait to see the light at the end of the tunnel, go down there and light it yourself'

Take charge now. Go and light the whole road through the tunnel, not just the end. You can be *anything* and *anyone* you want. I truly believe that. When I look back on my life—where I came from and the path that I took to get here—I wonder how and why. I look at friends and colleagues who have not done all that they wanted to and ask "why?" Why not just do it? If there was something I wanted to do, I did it. I jumped in feet first and had a go. It did not always work out exactly as planned, but that was part of the experience I needed. You never know the who, what, when or where something is going to be a lead for you. You have to just go for it and jump in.

For 13 years I was a pyrotechnician (I fired off fireworks at shows), working casually for a Brisbane fireworks company. It was very much a male-dominated industry, but it was something I was interested in and wanted to do. The opportunity arose, and I went for it. I had a ball working hard and receiving the greatest buzz.

Look at everything and experience as much as possible in life. Pick what works for you, and go with your beliefs and passions. Live your dreams. Do not wait for happiness to come to you, go and grab it for yourself. Of course, you may not want to be a pyrotechnician! But consider what you are doing: what is working in you life, and what is not. Stop sabotaging yourself. Make the changes and relish the benefits.

'There is nothing either good or bad, but thinking makes it so, change your thoughts and you change the world.'

William Shakespeare

What is Aromatherapy

Firstly, it is important to realise that Aromatherapy is not a 'wave the magic wand,' quick-fix for the problems and challenges of life. It is a science in the use of essential oils. This modality has seen a dramatic increase in popularity over recent years, since we all relate well to our sense of smell. Aromatherapy is a modality of natural therapy that is seriously pleasant and easy to integrate into your life. Provided you follow the basic rules outlined in this book, you should not run into trouble. It is important to consult a qualified practitioner if you have questions. A qualified practitioner of Aromatherapy will be registered with one of the following professional associations:

The International Federation of Aromatherapists (IFA)
The Australian Traditional Medicine Society. (ATMS)

Aromatherapy, like all natural therapies, is very effective as a tool in preventative health care. In my clinic I always have a few clients who say they have tried everything else, but nothing worked, and so they are now trying something natural. That's okay, because they now have a chance to rectify their imbalances. In Naturopathy, we talk of a person's context, that is, how everything happening within their external environment influences their internal environment, and vice versa.

If you are going to feed your body foods of low nutritional value and overwork it—abusing in it any way—you can expect a low grade of health in return. With all areas of natural therapies, we prefer to work in the preventative field. Why wait to get ill? Natural therapies, in particular, Aromatherapy, are very easy to integrate into your work and home life In this way you have less chance of getting ill in the first place, because you are keeping your life more balanced.

Most of the information published and the work that practitioners do in clinics, focuses on the physiological effects of the essential oils. And, in my clinic over the years, I have utilised this aspect as well. Because people are still in many instances, looking to relieve physical symptoms quickly. The essential oils are very effective at relieving the symptoms of most ailments. But what we want to do is address the cause of the imbalance.

Essential oils have many talents, their most obvious use and most frequently cited being the physiological, where the essential oils are used to treat ailments like headaches, etc. Yet the physical healing qualities are such a small part of the oils' potential. The emotional or subtle side is less well known, yet it can be the side that gives the greatest benefits because the oils also treat the *emotional* causes behind the *physical* ailments.

So what are the essential oils? In basic terms, the essential oils are fragrant elements that can be taken from just about any part of a plant. Like the flowers, flowering tops, leaves, fruit rinds, seeds, bark, roots, resin and berries. And in some cases several different oils can be taken from one plant. The orange tree, for example, gives Neroli from the flowers, Petitgrain from the leaves and Orange from the fruit. Each of these three essential oils has its own distinctive personality and therapeutic properties. The cost of the individual essential oils relates to how difficult the oil is to extract, and to the quantity of plant material required to manufacture the oil.

Essential oils are highly volatile, so they evaporate quickly once exposed to the air outside the bottle. They are complex chemical mixtures of organic molecules, which are safe provided they are used with care and according to their instructions.

We all have different ideas of what smells attractive. A scent that I adore could be unpleasant to another person. Memories are linked to sense of smell, and when teaching I use the example that Lavender can be the most relaxing oil in the world. However, if a sinister person from your past, for instance, had worn the oil constantly that memory would arise whenever you smelled the oil. You would be unlikely to receive all of the relaxing benefits of the Lavender, and would probably be more on edge than relaxed. So go with scents that you personally find appealing. We are all individuals and the same scent can vary in effects between people, depending on individual chemical make-up. So again, what smells pleasant to me may not to someone else.

The essential oils are absorbed into the limbic system of the body through the olfactory bulb and cilia in the top of the nose. While the scent is around you, your nose can become saturated with the scent. When this happens, you get to the stage where you cannot consciously

smell the scent. It is like when you apply your perfume or cologne in the morning and, after half an hour, you cannot smell it any more. So you put on some more and keep doing so until you have a six-feet wide perfume cloud around you! But although you are not aware of the aroma, it is still having an influence on you. When you use your oil burner, for instance, after a while you will not consciously smell the scent unless you leave the room and then re-enter. Remember, the oil is still working. This also applies to any person who has lost, or who was born without, a sense of smell. Such people will not get to enjoy the aromas, but they will still absorb the essential oils and receive the benefits.

'Invite your fears in, then tell them to sit down and shut up!'

Sark

Oils Ain't Oils

Just because a substance is "natural" does not mean that you need not be careful. Essential oils have their own safety guidelines to follow, and if you abide by these, Aromatherapy essential oils are very safe.

But first you should ensure that what you are buying, is what you need. To receive the therapeutic benefits of the essential oils, you have to use *genuine* essential oils—not a synthetic duplication. The synthetics are usually known as perfume or fragrance oils. Some essentials are expensive to produce because of the quantity of plant material required to extract the oil. For instance, it takes approximately 30-40 roses to produce one drop of rose essential oil. Most people like the fragrance of roses and want to enjoy the benefits, so a synthetic is produced. But some unscrupulous traders try to sell synthetic versions as the real oils, or dilute the rose with another oil. Synthetic oils, fragrance or perfume oils, whichever you wish to call them, have similar aromas but **do not have the therapeutic properties possessed by genuine essential oils.** All references to oils in this book pertain to essential oils, and not synthetics. So ensure you get what you want.

Here are a few pointers concerning what to look for when purchasing an oil: buy your oils from a reputable dealer, not from the corner markets. Ask questions about the qualifications of the person selling the oil if necessary, to ensure quality oils are purchased. You will be disappointed if you do not receive the benefits that you are expecting. By rights, if it is a genuine essential oil, it should have the following information on the label:

√ The common name of the essential oil and the botanical name of the originating plant. The botanical name is the Latin, hard to pronounce name. I have listed the Latin names of the essential oils I use in the latter pages.

√ Any poisons safety information; some essential oils are scheduled as poisons in Australia, and should carry the appropriate advice.

√ The concentration of the oil, 100 per cent is just that. Always look for small writing that may indicate dilution with jojoba oil etc. It is reasonable for the more expensive essential oils to be diluted in jojoba oil, for instance. But this must be labelled correctly. There is a big difference between the cost of a diluted and the cost of a 100 per cent oil.

√ A use-by date and an indication of the oil's expected life span.

√ The part of the plant used to manufacture the oil, as different parts of the plant yield different qualities of essential oil.

√ Essential oils are always stored in amber or blue glass bottles to protect the oils. Do not purchase essential oils in clear glass bottles.

Storage of Essential Oils

Always store essential oils in a cool, dry, dark, place away from heat and light. The oils do not like extremes, so do not put them into the refrigerator or store them near heats in excess of 30 degrees.

Essential oils are volatile and will evaporate if not kept in bottles with tight lids. The oils are also flammable, and are to be kept away from naked flames. Wooden boxes are excellent for storing essential oils, and maintain the quality and life span of the oils.

Safety with Essential Oils

√ Do not apply pure essential oil directly onto the skin, or take internally, unless advised by a qualified and registered Aromatherapy practitioner.

√ Never exceed the recommended dosage.

√ Do not use exactly the same oil all of the time, as you can build up a resistance to the oil and find it not as effective. If you use synergistic blends of the oils, you will find them more effective. A synergy is a blend of three or more essential oils in the same mix that complement each other and address the disorder you want to treat.

√ Working with children calls for a lower dosage. For adults, use a 3 per cent dilution, which is about 60 drops of essential oil to 100ml of carrier oil. And for children and people with sensitive skin, use 20 drops of essential oil per 100 ml. Those drops are in total. So if you have three different essential oils in the blend, you do not add 60 drops of each for an adult strength massage oil. It would be 60 drops in total.

√ Follow the safety guidelines on the following page if you are pregnant, have high blood pressure, or epilepsy.

Essential oils can bring powerful benefits to your life, and are considered safe. But we do have to abide by some rules.

Some essential oils are to be AVOIDED by people with certain conditions, and these are set out below:

Essential Oils Not To Be Used

Condition	Essential Oil
Pregnancy	Basil, Clary Sage, Cedarwood, Sweet Marjoram, Peppermint, Cypress, Fennel, Rosemary, Rose.
High Blood Pressure	Rosemary, Thyme and Sage.
Epilepsy	Rosemary Thyme and Sage.
Sensitive Skin & Allergies	Basil, Lemon, Cinnamon, Clove, Lemongrass, Thyme and Tea Tree. *If applied to the skin.*
Photosensitisation *This refers to the application of essential oils onto the skin, before exposure to the sun. Vaporisation of these oils does not have the same effect.*	Bergamot, Lemon, Cold Press Lime.

How to use the Essential Oils

Oil Burners

I prefer to use electric oil burners. They are safe, efficient and you do not have the worry of naked flames and water. The *Aromamatic* electric oil burners are safe and free of mess and worry. In the morning or in preparation for a meeting etc, select the essential oils of your choice and add a total of 10 drops into the burner. Plug in the burner and turn it on. There is no need to use water and candles. The recommended electric oil burners carry the C-Tick indicating that they do not cause interference with nearby communication and electrical equipment. The ceramic bowl produces just enough heat to release the scent of the essential oil.

ELECTRIC OIL BURNER

If you prefer the romance of the candle in the traditional oil burners, place a little water in the top of the bowl above the candle. Add 5-10 drops of essential oil onto the water and light the candle. Remember, never leave a burning object unattended, and never leave the water in the burner to burn dry. Candle oil burners are safe to use, but do not leave them unattended. To prevent any risks and worry, use an electric oil burner like the *Aromamatic*. Both the electric and candle burners can be cleaned easily by wiping the bowl with a damp towel once you have finished with the burner.

CANDLE BURNER

Inhalations

Just like the traditional childhood steam treatment, add 5-10 drops of essential oil to a bowl of steaming water. Then place a towel over head and bowl and inhale the vapours for a few minutes. Or, add 3-4 drops of essential oil onto a handkerchief, and hold this near the nose for a few minutes and inhale the vapours.

Body Sprays and Air Fresheners

For those times when you cannot or do not want to use a burner around the office, at home or in the car. You can prepare a blend for those trips between home and the workplace, or for that quick mist or recharge between breaks in the day. The easiest way to blend is by placing 50 drops of essential oil with 50 drops of essential oil soluboliser into 100ml of water. That is, 50 drops of essential oil in total, not 50 drops of each oil, if you are blending a few essential oils together. Add a little at a time, shake well, and enjoy.

Aromatherapy for travel. Mist face and body as required. If you are unable to have an oil burner in the workplace or home, you can make up a room freshener using the same principle as above.

Start with a spray bottle, say 100ml of filtered water, some essential oil soluboliser, or, as a last resort, a pure alcohol like vodka, and the essential oils you are going to use. The blending is quick and easy, and you still get the benefits.

My favourite recipe for a harmonious, enthusiastic environment room freshener, is as follows:

This makes up 100ml of spray.

20 drops of Bergamot
20 drops of Grapefruit
10 drops of Nutmeg
10 drops of Pine

There are about 20 drops of essential oil to 1ml, so it is easy to work out dilutions. Never exceed a 3 per cent dilution in a spray, as a stronger dilution will not necessarily bring better results.

Compresses

A compress is a quick, effective, easy, and practical application of the essential oils. First, you have to decide if a cold or warm compress is appropriate. For instance, a hot-and-bothered headache will ease with a cool Lavender compress. Use 5 drops of essential oil in 200mls of water. Place a cloth on the surface of the water and then ring it out. Lay it over the affected area of your body for about 15 minutes. For a warm compress, which is useful for a foggy head and/or sinus congestion, repeat the same method using warm instead of cold water.

Massage

Massage is considered one of the oldest and simplest of all medical treatments. It is an easy process to integrate into your life, and it can procure and maintain good health. You will gain the benefits of the essential oils simply by rubbing them, diluted, onto your skin. They will be absorbed dermally and you will also receive the benefits via inhalation.

To blend a massage oil. Use between a one and three per cent dilution of the appropriate essential oil, to the carrier oil. The carrier oils recommended are cold-pressed vegetable oil base, like almond or apricot kernel. On adults, use a 3 per cent dilution, which is about 60 drops of essential oil to 100ml of carrier oil. And for children and people with sensitive skin, use 20 drops of essential oil per 100 ml.

NB: Never use mineral-based oils, such as baby oil, as carrier oils in Aromatherapy. They do not carry essential oils effectively and can cause sensitivity problems for many individuals.

Baths

Baths are a delicious way to enjoy the benefits of Aromatherapy, receiving the benefits by absorbing them through the olfactory system (your nose) and your skin. It is like sitting in a wonderful inhalation. Breath in, and enjoy the benefits. The essential oils first need to be diluted into a base oil. You can use a normal carrier oil, but this floats on top of the water and makes a mess in the bath. If you use a dispersing bath oil base, which is a water-soluble base, there is

no mess and you absorb the essential oil more efficiently. The blending is as for the massage oils. On adults, use a 3 per cent dilution, which is approximately 60 drops of essential oil to 100ml of carrier oil. And for children and people with sensitive skin, use 20 drops of essential oil per 100 ml. Then add about 10mls of that mixture to the bath.

Foot Baths

If you are not fortunate enough to have a bath, do not despair. You can still make a foot bath. No fancy implements are needed, a bucket of water will do the trick. You can blend the essential oils, as described above, and add them to the water. If you are going to go home and be mindless after work, try being mindless with your feet in a bucket of warm, relaxing, aromatic oils. This will improve the quality of your evening or relaxation time. Very few people these days have the quantity of relaxation time they used to have 10 years ago, so at least make yours good quality time. It is worth the five minutes it takes to make up a foot bath.

In the Car

Scent a tissue with a few drops of essential oil and place into the air-conditioner or heating ducts to release the scent. Scent cotton wool balls and place them in the ashtray or under the seat of the car. You can also purchase decorative, small, wooden blocks that absorb the essential oils and release them slowly. The scent lasts for a day or days, depending on the method and the oil used, and you receive the benefits of the particular essential oils.

As a Perfume

The essential oils can be blended to make a perfume. It is easy, and there are two basic methods to choose from. Either blend 3 per cent of essential oils into a Jojoba base oil or into a perfume base made from pure alcohol and orris root powder.

A personalised Aromatherapy perfume or cologne can become an essential part of your life. You may be a shy person who needs to draw on extra courage sometimes and you could have your own personal blend that suits just you. Those around you will think that you simply enjoy wearing interesting perfumes. But you will know that you are receiving the emotional benefits of the fragrances as well.

Shower

Start or end the day with an aromatic shower. There are two basic methods. The first is to place a few drops of essential oil onto the wall of the shower, not in direct contact with the water, below the shower rose, for instance. The heat of the water picks up the essential oils and you are immersed in a giant inhalation. The essential oils used, will reflect the outcome of the shower.

The other method is to blend your essential oils in a non-detergent, non-scented gel base. Use this as a moisturising, aromatic, bath gel that not only cleans, but enhances your mood and emotions. It could be relaxing or invigorating, mentally stimulating or sensual. The choice is yours.

Miscellaneous Uses

In the majority of cases, essential oils will not stain, but you do need to use common sense. If you are using oils like Vetiver or Patchouli that are dark-coloured, they can stain a little. But if a virtually clear oil like Lavender is used, you can easily place a couple of drops onto fabric. If I want to use an oil on the run, and I do not have a body mist made up, I will put a drop of essential oil onto my collar and breathe it in like an inhalation. The scent remains around me and I receive the benefits.

When I change the sheets on my bed, I place a few drops of a blend I have created using sensual and relaxing essential oils onto the sheets. Every time I climb into bed I am greeted by an intoxicating aroma that takes me off to where I want to go.

You can also add a few drops of essential oils to the final rinse of your wash, to give your clothes a fragrant wash. A friend of mine places a drop of Lavender onto the car seat so that her four-year old can have a relaxed journey.

The uses are only limited by your imagination. So expand your mind and play.

The Essential Oils
In the workplace

Ever thought about the fact that you spend so much of your life at work? It does not matter what kind of work you do, from the retail environment, to the office or doctor's surgery, all work places can be enhanced by using essential oils. Physical, emotional and business health can be weakened if teams of people are working at levels that are taxing them. It is pretty hard to find nowadays, anyone working with a lighter workload than they had five years ago. I know myself, the demands of owning a business are enormous. However, with a little thought you can bring a more relaxing yet productive environment into the workplace with the help of essential oils.

The application of essential oils into the work environment is very practical. Apart from the usual aspect of the physiological benefits of essential oils where, for instance, Basil and Lemon essential oils are classed as cephalics (which means to stimulate and clear the mind), the subtle or emotional side of the essential oils can also be integrated and prove beneficial. On a physiological level, Lemon essential oil was found in one study to reduce typing errors by 54 per cent, when the essential oil was vaporised into the air.(1) On the subtle emotional level, Lemon can be used to help people become more rational, focused and clear in their decision making.

Within the workplace, essential oils can be incorporated to enhance the atmosphere for the workers and clients and therefore benefit the business. Imagine conducting meetings where the participants band together in a positive atmosphere, allowing everyone to express their opinion and come to agreements and strategies with the minimum of fuss. The situation in the past may have been that staff were uncooperative, allowing egos and emotions to get in the way. This may have meant wasted time and energy, or a hindrance to you or the business in making new improvements and implementing change. Some people can be negative or just resistant to anything that you present, so utilise the talents of the essential oils to remove that resistance. Take the time to create an atmosphere where all participants are going to be more willing to engage in a positive manner, where everyone feels comfortable and free to express their opinion. This will allow the business, the clients and the team members to grow and succeed.

Combining essential oils into a synergy of say Black Pepper, Patchouli and Rosewood, could create an environment where the participants feel united and receptive, motivated and ready for change. (Exact recipe in recipe chapter). This would be an exciting blend to infuse during a sales meeting for instance. Or, if a new employee was meeting the rest of the team for the first time, Basil, Peppermint, Lime and Cedarwood (exact blend in recipe chapter) would help the new person feel confident to express her/himself freely. Everyone would then feel grounded and secure with the new person joining the team, and it would be a stimulating meeting environment where all members were ready to tackle the tasks ahead.

What if you are the one going to a meeting away from your workplace, perhaps to give a presentation. The chances are they do not have an oil burner infusing essential oils into the environment like you do, (being the proactive, go-getting businessperson that you are). So, try to at least prepare yourself. Make your own power blend to "mist" yourself on the way to the meeting. It could contain Ginger, Grapefruit, Nutmeg and Pine (exact blend in recipe chapter). You arrive, wow! standing tall, energised, and self assured. You are ready to take on the world feeling optimistic and focused, but in an emotional space ready to listen and negotiate.

Be in control of the environment. Set the atmosphere in advance so that the air within the meeting room greets all of the participants, putting them in the mood for constructive work.

The following are some combinations that may be useful. These combinations are blended from the emotional aspect, not just from the usual physiological one. Basil is a mental stimulant and excellent for nervous tension and nervous exhaustion, but it is also renowned for helping people express themselves. The dilutions provided are suggestions for oil burners. Depending on your own situation, you may choose to change blends. These are my suggestions, but only you know your environment and the people in it. Follow the process, "tease you nose" and enjoy creating your own combinations that suit you and your organisation uniquely.

OIL BURNER RECIPES

Morning Starter

Stimulate your mind and emotions to all that is possible for the day, allowing inspiration and happiness to evolve in your life.

May Chang	Stimulating	- 3 drops
Mandarin	Happiness	- 4 drops
Myrrh	Inspirational	- 3 drops

Afternoon Reviver

Ease the stresses and be invigorated. Draw on the warmth of the spices to recharge energies and complete the day with the same vigour you commenced with.

Spearmint	Invigoration	- 2 drops
Ginger	Stamina	- 3 drops
Lime	Eases Stress	- 3 drops
Nutmeg	Increases Energy	- 2 drops

Brainstorming Sessions

Prepare yourself and your team for an invigorating, creative, and inspirational time where all can expand the mind and explore outside the box.

Spearmint	Invigoration	- 2 drops
Juniper	Preparation	- 2 drops
Rosemary	Creativity	- 2 drops
Myrrh	Inspiration	- 1 drops
Lemongrass	Expansion	- 3 drops

Harmonious, Enthusiastic Environment

Happiness and optimism are abundant when you work with these essential oils. The environment and everyone in it feels confident and strong, and has that passion for life.

Bergamot	Cheerfulness	- 2 drops
Grapefruit	Re-balance	- 3 drops
Nutmeg	Increases Energy	- 3 drops
Pine	Raise Self Worth	- 2 drops

United, Motivated, Go-getters

Motivate your team and enjoy the way it is receptive to new ideas. Work together, united in a common direction and goal.

Black Pepper	Direction	- 2 drops
Patchouli	Unity	- 2 drops
Rosewood	Receptivity	- 6 drops

Power Blend

Draw on your stamina and reserves of inner strength to push through barriers, finding your confidence and sense of self worth recharged and your outlook absolutely positive and optimistic.

Ginger	Stamina	- 2 drops
Grapefruit	Optimism	- 3 drops
Nutmeg	Increases Energy	- 2 drops
Pine	Raise Self Worth	- 3 drops

Induction Blend

It is important when you are introducing someone or something into the environment, that everyone feels comfortable and receptive to the change. People are then comfortable to express themselves and divulge any concerns. Remember, some people can fear change, so make the environment as comfortable as possible for all.

Basil	Self Expression	- 3 drops
Peppermint	Purpose	- 3 drops
Lime	Eases Stress	- 3 drops
Cedarwood	Courage	- 1 drop

Enhancing Team Loyalty and Unity

Inspiring a team to work together with passion and towards a common goal is essential, but this passion needs to be grounded. Don't get trapped with the mental material, manifest the ideas presented.

Basil	Self Expression	- 2 drops
Vetiver	Centred	- 1 drop
Jasmine	Live with Passion	- 3 drops
Patchouli	Unity	- 4 drops

Raising & Inspiring Team Spirit

Raise self confidence and self worth, allowing yourself and others to feel comfortable expressing themselves. Nurture and empower yourself and the team. Enjoy tapping into the pure essence of your being. Access courage and determination to stay focused on tasks at hand.

Basil	Self Expression	- 2 drops
Peppermint	Purpose	- 3 drops
Cedarwood	Courage	- 2 drops
Lavender	Nurturing	- 1 drop
Pine	Raise Self Worth	- 2 drops

Re-balancing the Extremes

For those who live on the roller-coaster of life, as much as it is fun to ride, it can be exhausting for you and others around you. Re-balance by integrating all areas of your life, and live and work in a state of inner peace, free from frustration.

Geranium	Re-balance	- 5 drops
Eucalyptus	Integration	- 3 drops
Ylang Ylang	Peace	- 2 drops

Breaking Patterns

Let go of the baggage that you have carried with you and be invigorated. Then you can allow the new experiences and adventures to enter your life. It takes courage and a sense of determination to be receptive to the idea of integrating change.

Spearmint	Invigoration	- 3 drops
Cedarwood	Courage	- 2 drops
Rosewood	Receptivity	- 4 drops
Chamomile	Let Go	- 1 drop

Motivational Meeting

Sometimes we need that kick-start to access the drive and determination we require to accomplish our goals. Enjoy the invigoration and recharge energies as you stay focused on your direction and pursue your passions.

Ginger	Stamina	- 1 drop
Nutmeg	Increase Energy	- 2 drops
Spearmint	Invigoration	- 3 drops
Jasmine	Live with Passion	- 2 drops
Black Pepper	Direction	- 2 drops

Basic Staff Training

Keep a team in training, being optimistic and receptive to the ideas and systems presented. Ring that feeling of happiness, enjoyment and stimulation to the environment.

Bergamot	Cheerfulness	- 2 drops
Grapefruit	Optimism	- 2 drops
May Chang	Stimulating	- 2 drops
Rosewood	Receptivity	- 4 drops

Reduce the Seriousness and Lighten Life

Grimness is dangerous to a person's inner health. A light spirit eases stress and brings a sense of peace. Enhance your life by allowing yourself to be light-hearted.

Bergamot	Happiness	- 2 drops
Orange	Remove Seriousness	- 4 drops
Ylang Ylang	Peace	- 2 drops
Lime	Ease Stress	- 2 drops

Heart-Nurturing Environment

From time to time we need to be in a more heart-nurturing environment, to feel safe and be able to let go. To break patterns and regain our passion for life and everything in it.

Rose	Love	- 2 drops
Lavender	Nurturing	- 4 drops
Jasmine	Live with Passion	- 2 drops
Ylang Ylang	Peace	- 2 drops

Setting Budgets

In business and in life, budgets are an essential tool to help us stay focused on our goals. We have to be rational and work together, being united to achieve the positive results we desire.

Patchouli	Unity	- 1 drop
Lemon	Rationality	- 2 drops
Juniper	Preparation	- 2 drops
Clary Sage	Clarity	- 3 drops
Eucalyptus	Integration	- 2 drops

Releasing Anger

For those who get a little "hot under the collar" at times, let it go, cool off, and find your inner peace again.

Ylang Ylang	Peace	– 3 drops
Lime	Ease Stress	– 5 drops
Eucalyptus	Integration	– 2 drops

Relieve Impatience

Remove any unnecessary attachments to having only your expectations met. Let go and trust that everything is happening at the right pace and in the right time and in the right way. Anxiety melts away when you choose to let it go. Frustration and impatience achieve nothing except ill health in the long term.

Palmarosa	Adaptability	– 4 drops
Chamomile	Let Go	– 1 drop
Clove	Attachment	– 2 drops
Marjoram	Anxiety	– 3 drops

Improve Memory

Stay stimulated and focused in life. Expanding your life experiences allows you to use your mind and express what you think and feel. If you don't use it, you lose it. Enjoy using it.

Basil	Self Expression	– 3 drops
Lemon	Rationality	– 2 drops
Lemongrass	Expansion	– 1 drop
May Chang	Stimulating	– 4 drops

Grounding

Ever been in the situation where you are doing everything, but doing nothing? When you have a full mind to contend with, stay grounded and balanced so that you can achieve all you desire.

Vetiver	Centred	– 3 drops
Cedarwood	Courage	– 3 drops
Geranium	Re-balance	– 4 drops

Mental Focus

Stay clear and in the conscious mind, ever mindful of the roles you play in the game of life. Be invigorated while you preserve energies, not allowing yourself to be drained on any level.

Petitgrain	Consciousness	– 4 drops
Spearmint	Invigoration	– 3 drops
Clary Sage	Clarity	– 3 drops

Relieve Overwhelmed Feelings

Learning how to use oils to stay centred through times where you feel overwhelmed, eases stress. It also allows you to move between your conscious and subconscious mind to focus on the positives in the situation and to rationalise what is actually happening.

Petitgrain	Consciousness	– 5 drops
Lime	Eases Stress	– 2 drops
Vetiver	Centred	– 3 drops

Creativity

Look outside the box, expanding your mind and environment so that you can access and express your creative ideas. Be passionate in life.

Rosemary	Creativity	– 4 drops
Lemongrass	Expansion	– 2 drops
Jasmine	Live with Passion	– 2 drops
Basil	Self Expression	– 2 drops

Increasing Productivity

Live in the now, with vitality and stamina. Work united to find those extra reserves, driving yourself and others to achieve all that is possible.

Patchouli	Unity	– 3 drops
Thyme	Willpower	– 2 drops
Ginger	Stamina	– 2 drops
Jasmine	Live with Passion	– 2 drops

Negotiating Environment

When you need to be the diplomat and negotiate deals, you need to ensure that your ideas and terms are received positively, and that all parties are comfortable with what is achieved in the process. The win/win situation.

Basil	Self Expression	– 4 drops
Cinnamon	Introversion	– 3 drops
Thyme	Willpower	– 2 drops
Vetiver	Centered	– 1 drop

Relaxing Environment

That wonderful sense of peace can be achieved, bringing good health and prosperity to those around. Use the essential oils to prevent anxiety and stay balanced through even the most trying times.

Lime	Ease Stress	– 4 drops
Marjoram	Anxiety	– 3 drops
Geranium	Re-balance	– 2 drops
Vetiver	Centred	– 1 drop

Emergencies & Shock

In emergencies of any description, you need to stay grounded and focused. If you work in a team, you will work together, united and able to understand each others needs at the time. If you are alone in a situation, you will integrate all of your skills and draw on what is required.

Vetiver	Centred	– 2 drops
Tea Tree	Understanding	– 3 drops
Patchouli	Unity	– 2 drops
Eucalyptus	Integration	– 3 drops

Job Interview

Feel confident and emotionally protected when going into this kind of environment. Times of transition can be a little, or a lot, unnerving. Be true to your choice of being there in the first place, and go for it with determination.

Cypress	Transition	– 4 drops
Palmarosa	Adaptability	– 3 drops
Neroli	Choices	– 2 drops
Frankincense	Protection	– 1 drop

Releasing Negative Emotions

Let go and live. Be optimistic about the future and focus on the positives. During times of change, let go, move forward and reap the benefits. See past negative patterns as learning experiences, and move on.

Chamomile	Let Go	– 3 drops
Grapefruit	Optimism	– 3 drops
Cypress	Transition	– 4 drops

Releasing Tension

Ease the stresses of the day, and get lost in the childlike qualities of the citrus oils. Feel the benefits of being able to let go and leave everything behind.

Chamomile	Let Go	– 2 drops
Lime	Eases Stress	– 5 drops
Orange	Removes Seriousness	– 3drops

Relieving Frustration

Understand that frustrations occur when our expectations in a situation are not being met. Re-balance and remove your attachment to expectations. See that everything is happening the right way. Do the necessary planning and then "trust."

Tea Tree	Understanding	– 2 drops
Geranium	Re-balance	– 4 drops
Clove	Removes Attachment	– 2 drops
Juniper	Preparation	– 2 drops

Fear of Success

If you are living your dreams and not letting yourself get caught up in the past, you do not fear the future. You remove and prevent any anxiety from creeping in because you have courage and feel supported in your goals. You will succeed.

Marjoram	Anxiety	– 3 drops
Chamomile	Let Go	– 2 drops
Cedarwood	Courage	– 2 drops
Jasmine	Live with Passion	– 3 drops

Creative Visualisation

Activate your inner voice and intuition to expand, stimulating all areas of your life. Tap into your creative juices and allow them to flow.

Rosemary	Creativity	– 5 drops
Lemongrass	Expansion	– 3 drops
May Chang	Stimulating	– 2 drops

Relieving Boredom

It is simple, just do it. Jump feet first into anything and everything. Look at what is around you and just start. Use your energies to embrace life. By spending a little energy you will gain untold pleasure, just try.

Jasmine	Live with Passion	– 5 drops
Bergamot	Cheerfulness	– 2 drops
Nutmeg	Increases Energy	– 3 drops

Preventing Burn Out

Protect yourself, emotionally and physically, at times when you are in demand. This blend will help you stay balanced and energised, but peaceful.

Nutmeg	Increases Energy	– 4 drops
Frankincense	Protection	– 2 drops
Geranium	Re-balance	– 2 drops
Ylang Ylang	Peace	– 2 drops

Resolving Conflict

Understand that we are all individuals and we may handle things differently. Be warm and empathetic to others, listening to all of the relevant information, and then find a resolution to the conflict.

Tea Tree	Understanding	– 2 drops
Sandalwood	Contemplation	– 3 drops
Cinnamon	Warming	– 4 drops
Rosewood	Receptivity	– 1 drop

Enjoying the Extrovert Within

Locate and release the extrovert within. Feel safe and confident to explore the possibility of freeing a passion that may have been hidden for some time.

Pine	Raises Self Worth	– 2 drops
Rose	Love	– 2 drops
Black Pepper	Direction	– 2 drops
Cinnamon	Warming	– 4 drops

The Obsessive / Compulsive

Lighten up and be centred. Stop hanging on so tight and allow your mind to be free of obsessive thoughts.

Vetiver	Centred	– 2 drops
Palmarosa	Adaptability	– 3 drops
Orange	Removes Seriousness	– 5 drops

The Perfectionist

Re-balance extremes, and be realistic. The world will probably not end if everything is not done today. Release your attachments and ease the stresses that you create for yourself.

Geranium	Re-balance	– 5 drops
Clove	Removes Attachments	– 2 drops
Lime	Eases Stress	– 3 drops

Right Here, Right Now, Blend

This is a blend I created for a client named Bronwyn, who had been travelling overseas for a few months. Bronwyn was having trouble being happy about being back in Australia after the excitement of overseas. I needed to literally bring her back to the here and now, because although she was physically here, emotionally she was still away, which was causing her stress.

Jasmine	Live in the now	– 3 drops
Sandalwood	Contemplation	– 1 drops
Ylang Ylang	Peace	– 2 drops
Bergamot	Cheerfulness	– 2 drops
Patchouli	Unity	– 2 drops

Essential Oils & Emotional Benefits

Let's get in and Do it!

BASIL

Ocimum basilicium

Self Expression

The herb of love is used for the entrepreneurs in business and life who feel vulnerable and have trouble feeling comfortable expressing themselves. Basil is excellent in assisting you to trust your intuition and to be straightforward, shifting from a place of fear and confusion to one of clarity and positivity. Speak with enthusiasm and act with integrity from your heart, and then you speak your truth. This takes the unnecessary worry out of circumstances.

Basil is the oil for those who worry just for the sake of worrying. It is a refreshing and reviving essential oil that is traditionally used as a mental stimulant and for treating nervous tension and nervous exhaustion.

JOY!
click

BERGAMOT

Citrus bergamia

Cheerfulness

Feeling flat, tired or as if you have lost your spark for life? Use Bergamot to access your deeper levels and cheer your heart and soul. This is one of the most effective oils for depression, as it helps you regain confidence and motivation.

Bergamot helps you come to a space where you feel balanced and complete, relieving burnout, depression, apathy and that feeling of emptiness. It allows your mind to wander to a place where "cheerfulness" lives, where you can think lively thoughts and feel refreshed. Use this essential oil to brighten the room, establishing a productive and caring environment where everyone smiles.

Releasing repressed emotions allows you to express yourself in an uninhibited way, free from the frustrations of everyday life because you are allowing your energy to keep flowing. When your chi (vital energy) does not flow fluidly, you get unproductive, negative, addictive, behaviours and patterns. Break these patterns by expressing what you are feeling, as you feel it, and smile again.

climb every
mountain ...
... follow every
dream

CEDARWOOD

Cedrus atlantica

Courage

This is the essential oil to use when you need courage for the toughest situations in life, so you can be that "tower of strength".

Cedarwood gives you the willpower, persistence, and focus to keep going and to succeed. Do not wait for success to come to you. Access your courage and get what you want in life and business. Reinforce your ego in a positive way and don't let yourself be overlooked. As an oil taken from the wood of the tree, Cedarwood still keeps you grounded while you take charge, so that you do not become irrational or over-sensitive.

It is time to recognise negative situations and change them into learning experiences. You are the one in control. Tap into your courage and regain control over, and responsibility for, your life.

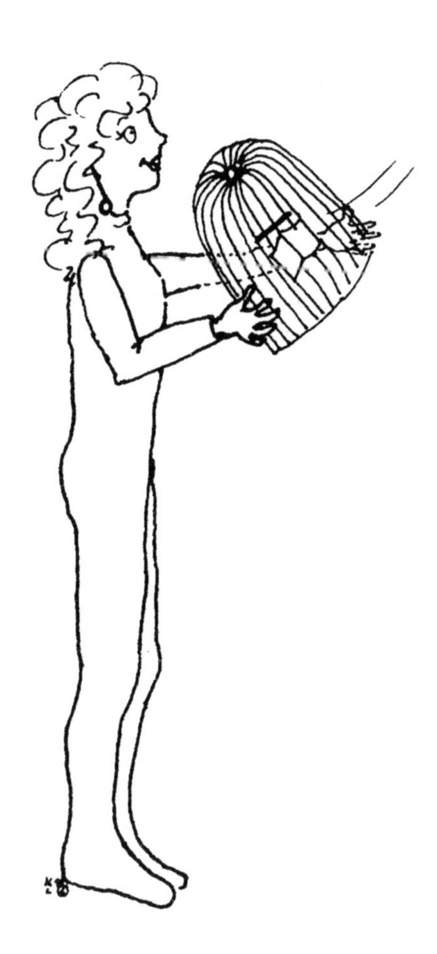

CHAMOMILE - GERMAN

Matricaria Chamomilla

Letting Go

German Chamomile helps break the negative patterns and old habits or ideas that are not working for you. Break the patterns that are limiting you and your business.

Use this oil for times when you are working so hard to control a situation, that you actually lose control. Let it go. You can care for others and yourself, but allow life's adventures to be just that, adventures. Do not carry them with you. The only way you can allow more "new" in, is to allow the "old" to leave. Stop being critical of yourself and others just because events or people are not living up to your expectations. They are, after all, your expectations and belong to you alone. Let them go and move on. Try another tack.

Because we are human, we act in a way appropriate to us with the information we have at the given time. Give people more information to work with or let it go. It is very limiting on your performance and that of your team, if you only work by "your" expectations.

CINNAMON

Cinnamomum zeylanicum

Coldness & Introversion

Warm yourself and regain that passion for life. Cinnamon's talent lies in its ability to be explosive and heat that emotional coldness out of you. Stop cutting yourself off and allowing yourself to feel isolated and numb. Explore your depths and access your untapped passion for life. See what you can be like when you "come out of your shell". There are plenty of people who are introverts playing the extrovert to survive in business and in life. Tap into your own inner strength and be who you really are or who you want to be.

Cinnamon is essential for times when you need to access that passion and enthusiasm for life, yourself and your team.

Help bring others out where *they* can feel comfortable and at *their* best. Cut through any spitefulness and like emotions to feel invigorated, alive and "out there."

CLARY SAGE

Salvia sclarea

Clarity

For times of emotional and mental confusion, mood swings and indecision, or you feel absent-minded, burnt out and weepy, Clary Sage regenerates, and restores harmony to your life.

Clary Sage is essential for when you need to be clear about what you want and how to get it. Do not be influenced by others. Stay clear and focused as to what you want. Access and work with your intuition to remove events that distract you from your path. Travel that road emotionally uplifted, but in a calm state. Clary Sage does not throw you over the top, but keeps you confident and steadfast in reality by connecting you to the earth.

Broaden your perception and your horizons, tapping into your subconscious to make those decisions clearly, and now.

CLOVE

Eugenia caryophyllata

Removes Attachments

Loosen your attachment to things that are inhibiting you from exploring new possibilities and experiences.

Go with the ever-changing environment and do not allow yourself to get too attached to one style or system. Remove the old and allow for new and exciting events to enter your life. Keep it simple, and be a living example and inspiration to others. This is the best way to achieve change. First change yourself and then the rest will follow.

Danielle Ryman writes: "*Clove, has an agreeable taste, and acts as a relaxant. Sucking cloves is a particularly good idea for those trying to give up smoking.*"(2)

CYPRESS

Cupressus sempervirens

Transition

When you move from one challenge and experience to the next, Cypress supports and protects you.

Drive forward with a sense of stability without feeling isolated, and feel safe and in balance during the move. Release the fears that prevent you from moving with change. Look outside the box for new possibilities and directions. This time of transition can either be positive if you go with it, or negative if you hold yourself back. Go forward, and stop people from dominating you and draining your emotional energy. Enjoy the ride.

Patricia Davis, renowned Aromatherapist and author, writes of Cypress oil being: *"helpful at times of transition, such as career changes, moving home or major spiritual decisions such as changing one's religion... Bereavement, or the end of a close relationship."* (3)

cool spritz
10 Things I want to do
Bungy jump from a helicopter
Climb Mount Everest!
Save the World today!
Find the Lost City of Atlantis
Fly to Venus!
spritz

EUCALYPTUS

Eucalyptus radiata

Integration

Remove the feeling of being hemmed in, and "hot under the collar". Look around, remove confusion and link all parts of the equation to make the whole you were seeking in the first place. Look, particularly, outside your normal environment. Go with your instincts and integrate new experiences. Remove constriction, release regrets and fear, be spontaneous, and give up negative habits. Seek and gain the freedom to do what you want.

Experience it all with the lightness of Eucalyptus. It is time to stop being predictable and argumentative. Negative emotions do not work for you, so change them.

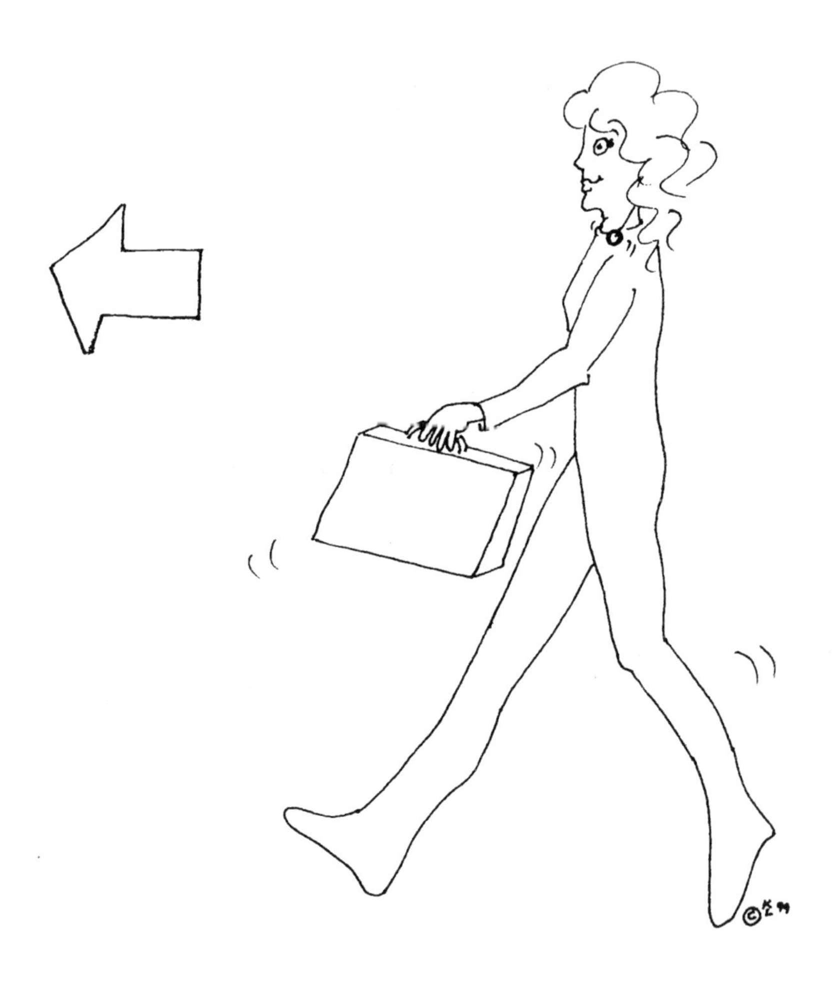

FENNEL - SWEET

Foeniculum vulgare dulce

Assertive / Completion

This is a lively and dynamic essential oil, removing feelings of being overwhelmed, bored and afraid of failure. It leaves you enlivened and able to regain that competitive edge.

Fennel was cultivated by the Romans and the gladiators, as they believed it would give them stamina and courage. Know your competition, do the ground work, and reap the benefits, for you will have the direction and focus to complete the task. Do not try to do everything at once, complete as you go and do not procrastinate. Attain your goals by concentrating on them and maintaining focus on the direction. Communicate freely and with confidence. Stay ahead in the game of life and go for it.

Move beyond your stagnant thoughts and remember your physical health. If you suppress your emotions, it can manifest as an ailment. So say it now. Be assertive and enjoy the fruits of life.

Frankincense
F

FRANKINCENSE

Boswellia carterii

Protection

Protecting yourself from agitation, worry and feeling overwhelmed, and helping you to keep focused on the tasks at hand is Frankincense.

Frankincense links you to your past and future, providing the link to how we perceive experiences. When you need to stay grounded it's great, especially if you tend to get caught doing everything but doing nothing. So busy doing "stuff" that, at the end of the day, you literally cannot see what you have finished. This kind of situation can cause frustration and anxiety. Integrate Frankincense to break free of attachments and reduce or prevent negative situations from occurring.

Become the wise person that you know you are. Use Frankincense to develop these traits, reap the benefits of freedom, and feel protected.

heart
head

GERANIUM

Pelargonium graveolens

Re-balancing

Feeling stressed and overworked, out of balance, emotionally up one minute and down the next?

Geranium delivers balance and symmetry to all areas of life. Perfectionists and workaholics benefit from using this oil, as it helps to reduce their extremes. Do not worry, it does not stop you from working hard, but it does help keep a balance between your heart and your head. Get rid of the "shoulds". For example, "I should do this or I should do that", or "I don't want to, but I should". This will allow you to balance the logical, analytical workaholic with the emotional, spontaneous, fun person you used to be and want to be.

This oil is essential in the workplace if you want to cope longer and work more efficiently. All work and no play makes us all stressed in some way.

Yahoo!
It's finished

GINGER

Zingiber officinalis

Stamina / Procrastinating

For the emotionally cold-hearted. You can have the best of intentions, but if you are out of contact with how the people you deal with are feeling, you will not deliver messages effectively.

Waiting for the right time to do what has to be done is physically tiring. So take the initiative because the right time never comes. Stop procrastinating, access your intestinal fortitude and just do it. Take the initiative and act on the task. You know the buzz you get when you push through, drawing on all levels of your energy to complete a task.

Utilise Ginger to draw on those hidden reserves of energy and stamina, reviving yourself physically with Ginger's warmth. If you have depleted your reserves of physical energy from long term over-expenditure of energy, it is time to recharge.

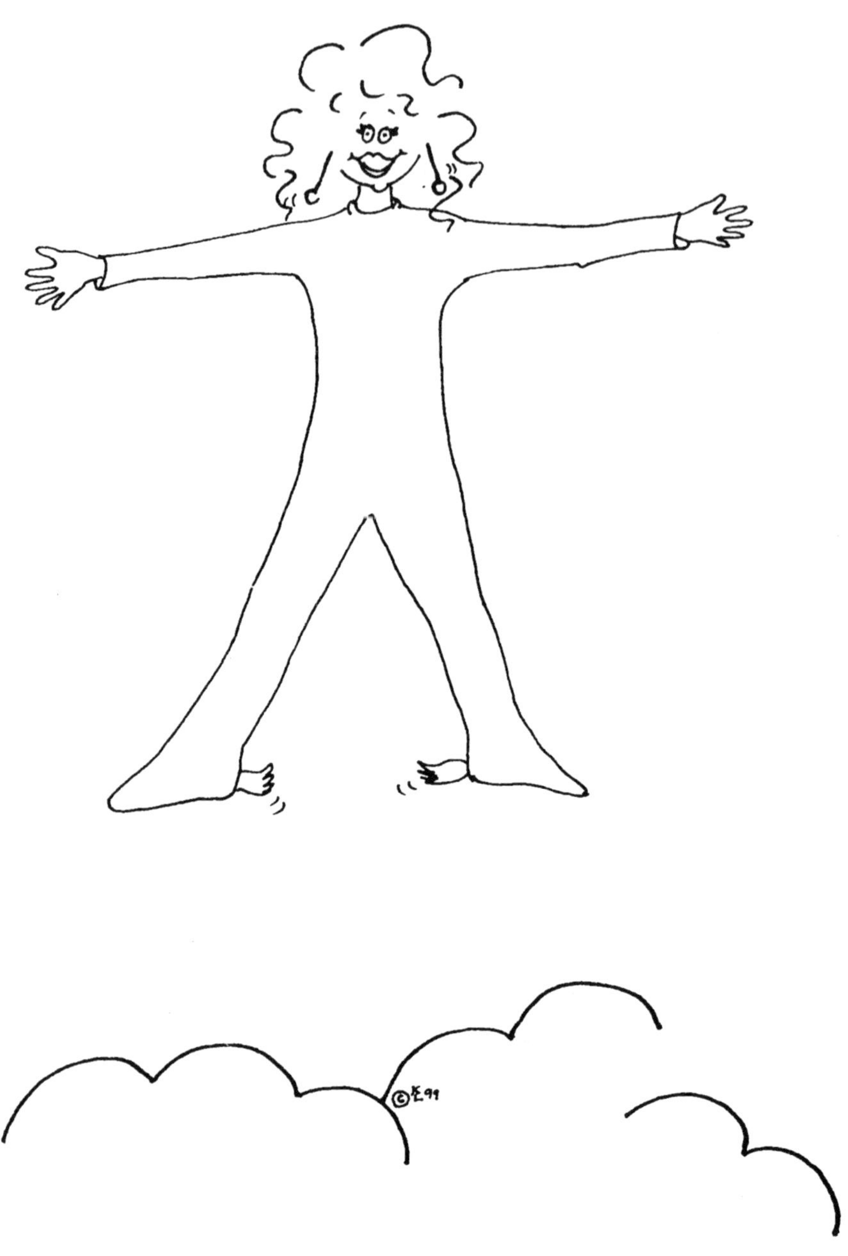

GRAPEFRUIT

Citrus paradisi

Optimism

Renew that zest for life. Stop feeling disappointed and wrung out. Grapefruit has a light, uplifting aroma that radiates optimism.

Focus on the positive and look after yourself better, nurturing yourself emotionally (and not with foods like biscuits). Grapefruit removes heavy, emotional feelings that can feed our addictions when expectations are not met. Stop being self-critical and blaming yourself. Use Grapefruit to get out of that mood and have some childlike fun again.

Emotionally purifying, Grapefruit releases self-doubt and frustration to bring in cooperation, positivity and the knowing that all will be okay.

JASMINE

Jasminum officinalis

Living in the Now With Passion

Live in the now. Stop worrying about what happened yesterday or what might come in the future. Just do what has to be done, now.

Jasmine removes feelings of depression, vulnerability and fear, and moves you to a place where you feel safe and supported. Jasmine re-ignites your passion for life by penetrating your deepest layers and releasing fears. Rebuild your trust in the process of life. Jump into life's challenges knowing that it is just another learning experience. You can choose to make it a positive or a negative one.

Jasmine is excellent for those working with creative projects, as it stimulates a fertile mind full of ideas and inspiration.

Athens
PUERTO RICO
London
ROMA
LUCERNE
PARIS

JUNIPER

Juniperus communis

Preparation

When you feel burdened and emotionally flat, you are so caught up in negative thoughts that you cannot plan for what is ahead, or effectively deal with what is happening now.

Clear your stagnant mind, release unwanted negative thoughts, and allow only positive experiences to enter. This is when you can make preparation for the emotional, physical, and spiritual challenges ahead. Take the time to make plans for future ventures, goals etc. It is only when we are not prepared that we get those "surprises" in life and business. Failure to release negativity and be prepared leads to an emptiness and dissatisfied state where guilt and low self-esteem abound.

Juniper is excellent for clearing negative energy from rooms, spaces, and your life in general.

CHICKEN
SOUP

LAVENDER

Lavender angustifolia

Nurturing

Peter Holmes (respected Herbalist and author) speaks of Lavender as being a *"Habit breaker and a crisis smoother"*. Lavender nurtures your heart, removes feelings of being overwhelmed and confused, and releases the "stuck" energy that can hold you back.

By nurturing yourself, you can take that step away from what may be stopping you, and you can start again. We forget, when we are out there saving the world or creating a new one, that if we do not take care of ourselves, we will not be able to keep going. At some stage we have to take stock and assess the damage we may be doing, not just physically, but emotionally. If you are feeling inhibited and/or over-sensitive, mentally and or emotionally stuck, Lavender provides a protective space where you can feel safe. Nurture yourself, and re-group your energies and start again, if necessary, so you can feel strong and confident, and be yourself. Lavender also helps you feel safe to be the extrovert or the confident introvert who can still express thoughts and feelings freely.

The calming presence and reassuring nature of Lavender provides a sanctuary in which you can ask for what you need.

LEMON

Citrus limonum

Rationality

Emotional outbursts can be very exciting, but rarely constructive. If you feel out of your depth and irrational, Lemon clears your head and enables you to focus on the task at hand. The fresh, tingly scent of Lemon lifts you emotionally, mentally and spiritually.

Traditionally used as a mental stimulant and for nervous tension and exhaustion, Lemon rescues your mind and releases self-doubt. Do not let yourself feel bogged down in life. Clear mental confusion, make those decisions, and focus. People with negative attitudes attract other, like-minded, negative people. If you "fire off" at someone or some thing, others around you will pick up on that energy and follow suit. This creates an environment of turmoil and apathy. Cool the atmosphere quickly with Lemon and get on with life.

LEMONGRASS

Cymbopogon citratus

Expansion

Remove limitations and restrictions, whether self imposed or not. Move beyond your normal boundaries and expand into the new. Lemongrass is an encouraging scent that lifts the spirit as you take action.

Be fascinated and curious about what else is out there and where you can go with it. Curiosity and wanting to expand your experiences allows you to expand into other realms, and retrieve new "things" and experiences to bring more passion and excitement into your life. Living outside of the box or out on the limb can be stimulating, exciting and more satisfying. It can also be the difference between living and just existing.

Remember, we all have different ideas of where the boundaries of our box are, but they can always be expanded.

LIME

Citrus medica

Eases Stress

Ease through changes without getting hot under the collar. If you are feeling furious, frustrated or stuck, cool down and refresh yourself with Lime essential oil. You can then ease off and handle the challenge with confidence and not fly off the handle, looking the fool. You will not suppress the feelings responsible, but you will channel them and use them constructively.

Lime takes you to that wonderful place where life is "sweet", fun and light-hearted. Sometimes we just need some time-out away from the heavy-going of business and life.

Ease into a state of relaxation with Lime.

MANDARIN

Citrus reticulata

Happiness

I always think of a child peeling a mandarin when I smell this aroma. I imagine their faces lighting up as they peel the fruit with ease.

Mandarin oil brings that happiness and childlike quality to life. Adults, remove that grimness and release abuse from your lives. Stop dwelling on the past and let's get back to enjoying life again. I know how much more productive I am when I enjoy myself.

Mandarin allows you to feel calm and soothed, but, at the same time, refreshed and inspired.

ANXIETY

MARJORAM

Marjorama hortensis

Anxiety

"Nobody loves me, everybody hates me, think I'll eat some worms".

Remember that ditty from childhood? I call this the "poor me" syndrome. You know, the feeling that no one cares or understands you. I'm doing it all alone and getting all worked up in the process. If you are feeling deprived of anything and everything—whether you really are or not does not matter, because in your reality you may be—use Marjoram to stop obsessive thinking, and remove that negative groove from your brain.

Once you see anxiety for what it is and release it, you are free to do what you want. Your mind can tie you to unhelpful negative emotions because that is easier than making the "scary" necessary changes. Marjoram is relaxing and calming and relieves the anxiety of life, helping you feel supported through the toughest times. And when you are offered support, remember to accept it.

Marjoram oil will preserve your energies for times when depletion can occur. Be the idealist and banish anxiety from your life.

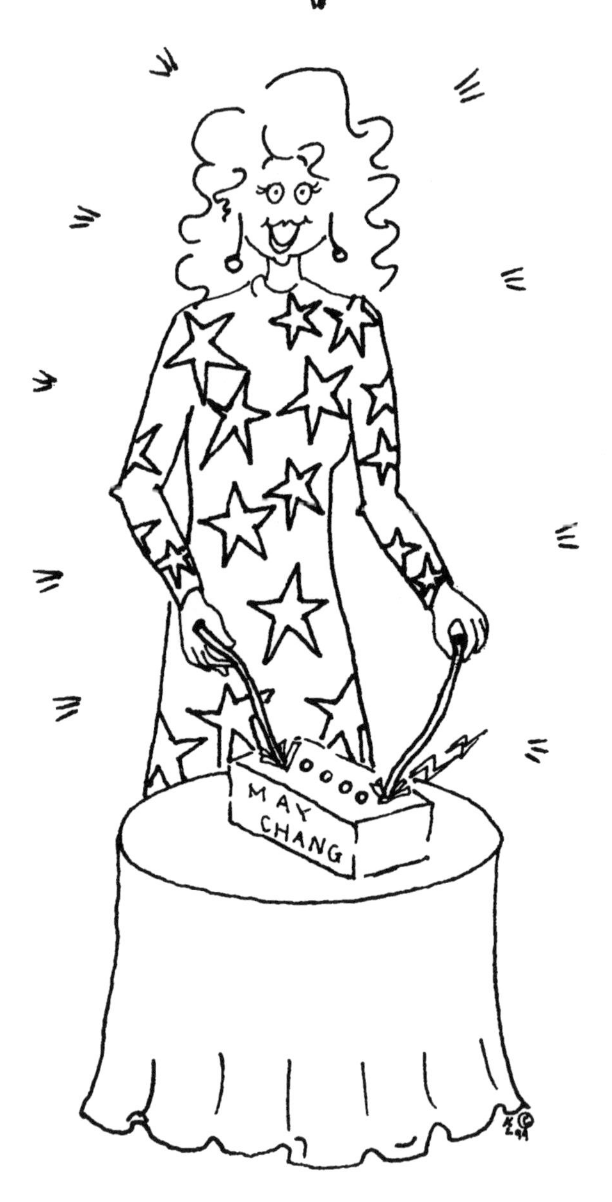
MAY
CHANG

MAY CHANG

Litsea cubeba

Stimulating

Stimulate and tone your senses with May Chang. It is ideal if you have been feeling flat and passed over for some time. Don't allow yourself to be overlooked. If you want to get somewhere or get something in life, you have to jump in and be seen and noticed.

Take the time to recharge yourself and your energy for life with May Chang. This vibrant, exciting and stimulating aroma lifts you without "throwing you over the top". Stay emotionally and physically "up", but relaxed at work and at home.

Essential for those who let a little "poor me" or "why me?" in periodically.

MYRRH

Commiphora molmol

Inspiration

Remove mundane thoughts and be inspired by what is possible if you only try. Tap into your dreams and visions to release a liberating strength and awareness.

Myrrh has an inner stillness that is soothing and grounds to the intellect. It is easy to fall into the trap of allowing limiting thoughts to constrict your personal and business growth.

Be inspired by life. Be curious, looking for the possible and the impossible. Use Myrrh when you want to be still and centred, but inspired internally, during the process.

NEROLI

Citrus aurantium var. amara.

Choices

Life is one grand bundle of choices that we make every second. Most of them are done unconsciously. Such as whether to breath and stay alive, how to handle a customer, what to wear or whether to keep reading this book. They are all choices, and some are harder to make than others.

Trust your intuition, listen to your gut instincts, and honour your choices. You make them with the information that is available to you at the time. Often they turn out to be great learning experiences, sometimes a challenge, and other times they are easy and enjoyable. Whatever they are, own them, and trust that they are right for you at this time. Enjoy the ride. If you wait for the right time to do something perfect, you may miss out on what you are after.

Just make the choice and do it. Everything and anything is possible in this world if you only choose to have a go.

NUTMEG

Myristica fragrans

Increases Energy

Re-kindle the fire within and warm your passion for life. Nutmeg is for chronic loss of emotional and physical energy.

Nutmeg stimulates and revitalises your body, and removes feelings of sluggishness, getting you going again. Lift the weight off your shoulders, conquer challenges and soar through encounters that may have stopped you in the past. Exercise is a good example. Sometimes you have to spend energy to get more energy, so envelop yourself in Nutmeg's aroma to maintain enthusiasm and passion in your exercise program. Going for an aromatic walk or run in the morning is an amazing start to the day.

Nutmeg warms life back into you. Be passionate about everything you do

Today's
Joke...

ORANGE

Citrus senisis

Seriousness

We all know that we have to be serious in certain life situations. But it is easy to get caught up and become too sombre. Business and life are serious, but if we are bogged down in the process, we get stressed and our work performance reflects this imbalance.

Sweet Orange is for the hardworking, efficient, perfectionist that constantly strives to achieve. They seem to know everything, and have little tolerance for other people's mishaps and learning experiences. Because they feel they are the only ones who can do "it" properly, they end up doing it all themselves, getting more stressed and more serious, grim and burnt out. They are no longer useful to anyone, especially themselves.

Lighten up and enjoy work. You can be responsible and efficient and have a light spirit at the same time. Be less gloomy, and find your sense of humour. Create a space where there is always a light at the end of the tunnel. If you cannot see the light, go down and light it yourself.

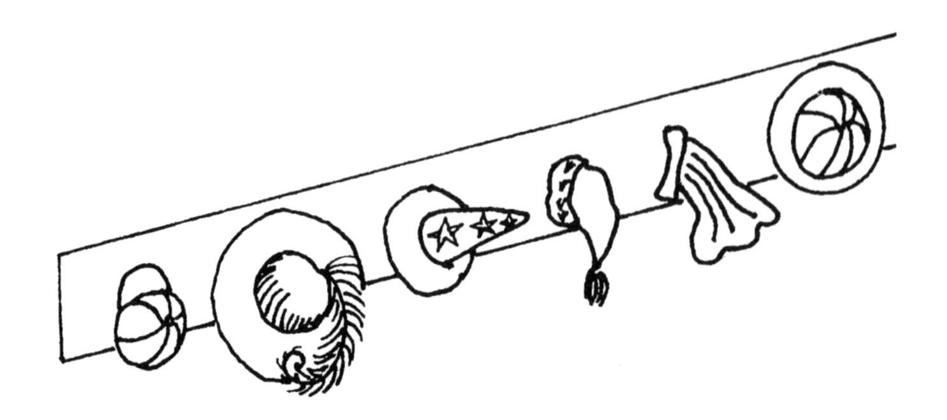

PALMAROSA

Cymbopogon martinii

Adaptability

Palmarosa helps you embrace change and let go. Sometimes we hang onto things so tight that they are ready to break at any instant. This masks our insecurities. We may have been hurt in the past, and now use this pattern as security, resisting and fearing change.

We live in an ever-changing environment where we have to let go of some "old" to provide a space for some "new". In business and in life, it is easy to get to a place of comfort. Everything proceeds in an acceptable manner, and we become complacent. It can be easier to stay with the old than change. This is the time when competition at work or in relationships shows up.

But if we are constantly growing and adapting to the changes in our work and home environments, success is assured. Life and work will never be boring, because you stay one step ahead of your competition and your environment. Shift your consciousness to a place where you enjoy being versatile.

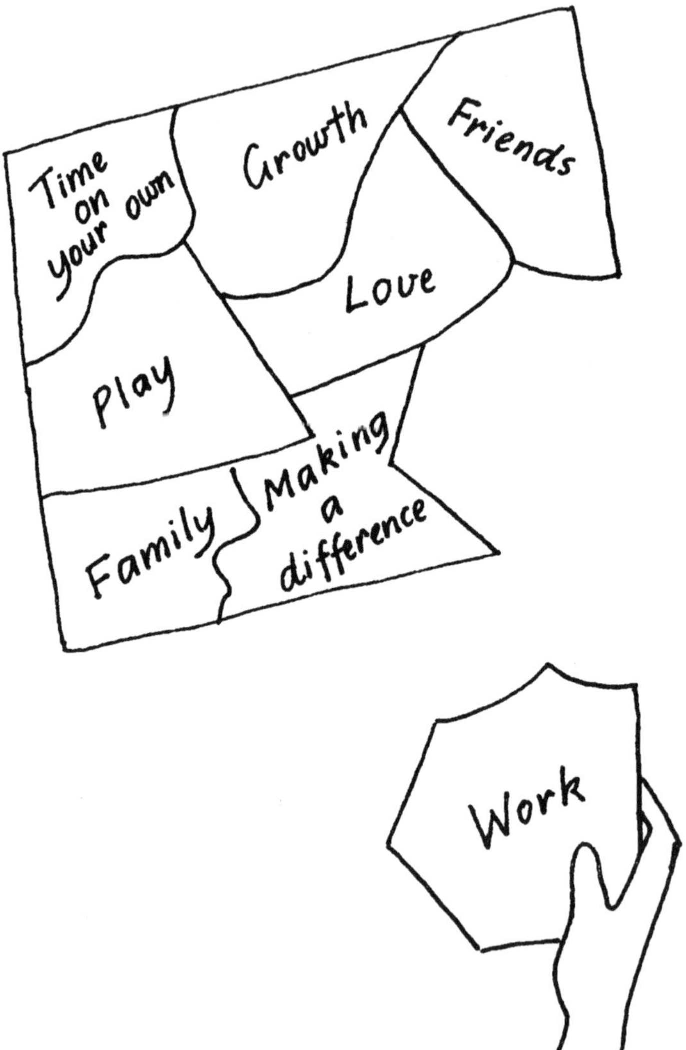

Time on your own

Growth

Friends

Love

Play

Making a difference

Family

Work

© KL '99

PATCHOULI

Pogostemon cablin

Unity

When you feel like you have lost your sensual pleasures and creative expression, Patchouli awakens a sense of peace that reaches into all areas of your life.

When you get trapped in the world of work or in any one area, draw all areas of your life together. When we are balanced and working in unity, we operate in a work environment more efficiently and enjoy our home life better, as well. The feelings that arise when all areas of life work together, are powerful. That is because our minds are united in working best at what we are doing, and energy is not scattered, but focused. Rise above self-imposed barriers and link your heart with your head.

Don't get ruffled and caught in the false ego. Stay self-assured, and realise your real strength lies in being you.

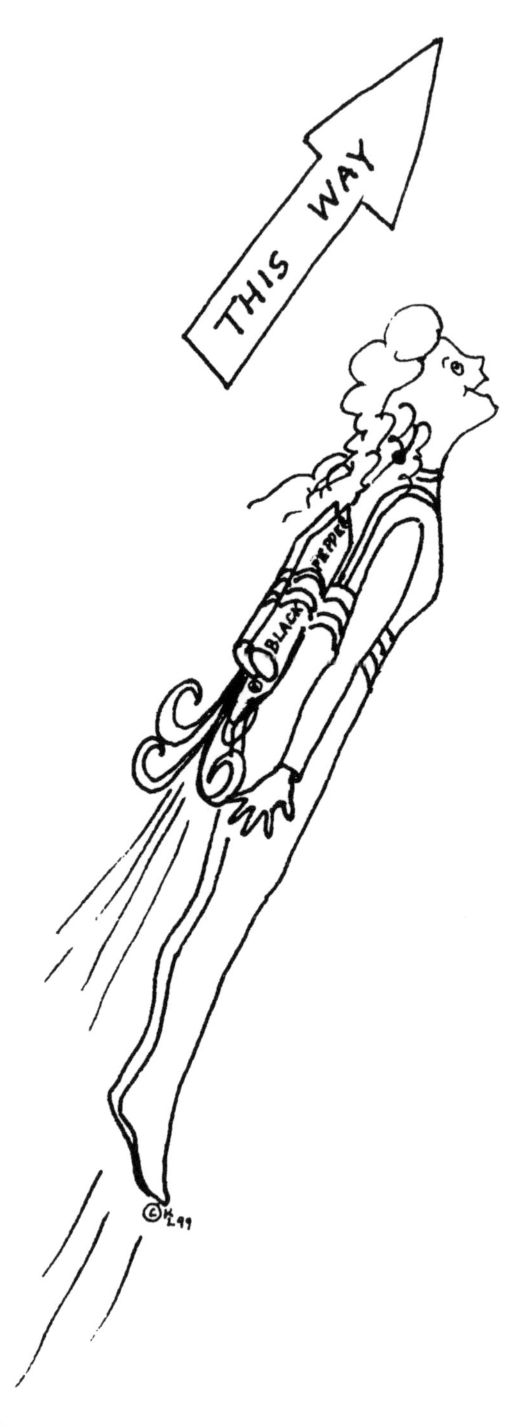
THIS WAY
BLACK
PEPPER

PEPPER - BLACK

Piper nigrum

Direction

Do you have an idea of where you want to go, but have run out of stamina to keep going?

The warmth of this essential oil assists in loosening blockages that may be holding you back. If you are trustworthy and loyal, but feel responsible for everything and everyone, use Black Pepper to stay focused on your path. Encouraging and helping others to do, and to be, their best is a positive aspect of your personality, but it can drain your own energy. Your ability to motivate others brings warmth and confidence to yourself and to your team. Your endurance at tasks can flow to others without draining you, if you allow it.

Black Pepper restores that secure outlook on life and keeps you going in the right direction.

PEPPERMINT

Mentha piperita

Purpose

Peppermint is about our sense of purpose. I believe we know where we are going, that it is encoded into us.

Ever noticed how you are presented with new experiences, or acquaintances at just the right time. It is as if it has happened just when we can handle it and not a moment sooner. Peppermint keeps us connected with our purpose in life and keeps our vital passion potent and ready to meet challenges that question your purpose and direction. Press forward through these challenges. Be excited and stay focused to achieve what you desire. Only we know ourselves what our purpose is in life.

Don't get caught up in other people's games. Be true to yourself. Go out on a limb and take risks if needed, or you may become dissatisfied with who you are, where you are going and what you are achieving.

PETITGRAIN

Citrus aurantium var. amara

Conscious Mind

Access thoughts or memories that have been stored and bring them to your conscious mind. The fresh stimulating fragrance of Petitgrain moves you into areas that you have not been accessing.

Whether suppressed or not, Petitgrain helps access these thoughts and memories and moves you into new surroundings. Focus on the positives that are being tapped and integrate the benefits. Do not be burdened by responsibilities.

Stay fluid and move between conscious and subconscious, accessing whatever is needed to achieve your success. Stay ever-mindful of the benefits

PINE

Pinus sylvestris

Self Worth

The strength of a pine tree firmly rooted in the ground but still strong and flexible, this essential oil instils positivity and raises self-worth, bringing peace to those who punish themselves. Living on guilt, they blame themselves for their own mistakes and for those of others as well. Pine is the best oil to utilise for protecting boundaries.

But learn that your essence is yours and others is theirs and what may be right for you may not be right for someone else. Accept and understand that we are all individuals, and have been thrown together to learn from each other.

Remember, you cannot save or rescue others, they have to do it for themselves. Feel strong in yourself, strong enough to honour and respect yourself. Move forward and let go of negative experiences and poor self-image. Enjoy your unique expression of life.

skippity
skip......

ROSE

Rosa damascena

Love

Rose renews the sense of well-being to all levels and areas of life.

Bringing comfort and warmth to those who have grown emotionally cold, Rose can knock down the biggest walls that we have built up for protection. Love flows deep, and we may have set our attitudes and beliefs around how we have experienced love in the past. Nothing from the past reflects on the future unless we choose to allow it to happen. So embrace the emotionally nurturing and sensuous benefits of Rose oil to discover and regain your passions in life.

Live life fully and do not just exist. It would be sad to go to your deathbed regreting that you did not love and live your life.

ROSEMARY

Rosmarinus officinalis

Creativity

Rosemary gladdens the spirit, invoking confidence to command creative energy into action.

Believe in yourself. You can manifest anything if you believe it. Be positive and stay focused. If you tell yourself that you are not creative, you will not be, but if you choose to explore your creative side, the possibilities are endless. This fragrance has a dynamic energy, spontaneous and extravagant, it frees you from the restrictions of life. Removing mental sluggishness, worry and fatigue, Rosemary, allows you to explore outside your everyday world.

Be creative, and paint your life the colours you want. Tap into the riches of your imagination and enjoy the changes that unfold.

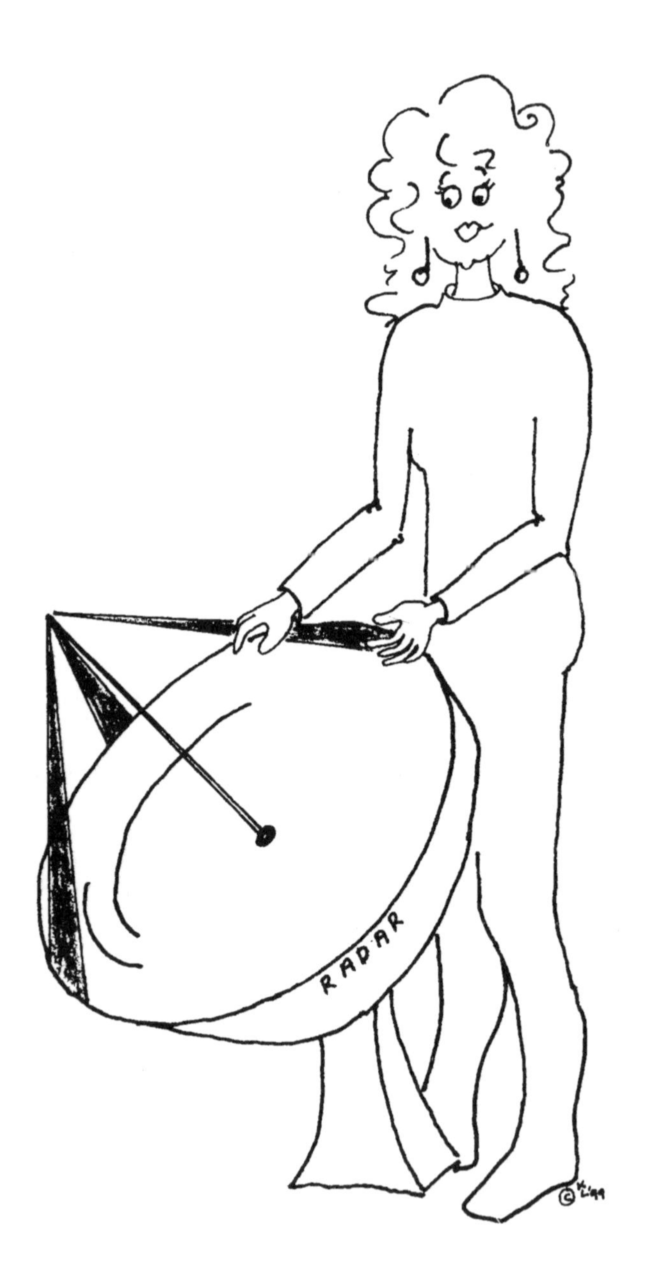
RADAR

ROSEWOOD

Aniba rosaodora

Receptivity

Staying receptive to all that life presents allows us to grow. Growing with balance, as a person or in business, is important. When staying grounded and trusting those often unused wise feelings, we heighten our perceptions and can be receptive to all that is present. It is being able to "see past the trees", and "through the fog" or whatever other catch phrase you choose to give it.

Rosewood utilises all of your senses to help you grow.

SANDALWOOD

Santalum album

Contemplation

I like to use Sandalwood for protecting my space and keeping me tranquil in times of turmoil.

Sometimes in life we need to go inside and contemplate. We get trapped working on the outside in the logical world, and lose our stillness inside. Doing all of the "stuff" that has to be done, but does not necessarily bring satisfaction. Sometimes we need to turn inside and just be; feel earthed and in ourselves. When working from inside, we have a peace and strength to see exactly how things really are.

You can use Sandalwood to help keep your space and aura strong, so you do not get caught up in everything around you. This will allow you to operate more efficiently and not take on the negative energies of others, their beliefs and attitudes.

SPEARMINT

Mentha spicata

Invigoration

Spearmint invigorates all levels of our being: emotional, physical and mental.

It is fresh and tingly, cool and soothing, it lifts you and helps keep a clear intention to preserve and utilise your energies efficiently.

Live the invigoration that Spearmint can bring to your life.

TEA TREE

Melaleuca alternifolia

Understanding

Raise the morale of yourself and your team, and take on a positive outlook in life.

Replace that victim mentality and feeling of doom and gloom with a feeling of understanding. Release the struggle in life by understanding what and why events happen. By finding patience and seeing other points of view, you bring tolerance and growth into an environment. And everyone feels secure and appreciated when not threatened.

Enjoy the chance to learn to understand yourself and the others in your life.

starting a garden nursery is the right thing to do.....
start a Garden Nursery

THYME

Thymus vulgaris

Willpower & Strength

As a fortifying oil, Thyme dispels despondency and negativity, giving those who withdraw the strength to emerge with self-confidence.

It removes fears and gives them strength to feel fulfilled and worthy. Possessing intuitive intelligence is a strength only if it is practised and put to use. You may have intuition, but its use may have been suppressed in times of challenge. Trust it now and draw on its power and influence to strengthen your will. Work with the positive aspects of willpower to draw on the dynamic energy and strength of yourself and your team.

During the 18th century, Thyme was thought to "resist madness and all diseases of melancholy". (4)

VETIVER

Vetiveria zizanoides

Centred

Vetiver is taken from the roots of the plant in the earth, and it allows us to return to the earth.

Vetiver is most useful at times when we are doing everything but doing nothing. Being the perfectionist, trying to do something so well that it never actually gets done. Your head is so full of everything you are trying to do that you are not grounded and centred, and are unable to manifest the changes needed, or even just get the work done. In a sense, mother earth is renewing us mentally and emotionally. Vetiver recharges your emotional and physical energies, and supports you in your endeavours.

Aromatherapist, Patricia Davis speaks of Vetiver as being useful in protecting one from becoming a "psychic sponge". If you are grounded and centred, you are less likely to take on everyone else's insanity.

YLANG YLANG

Canaga odorata

Peace

A voluptuous scent, full and plump with life, Ylang Ylang is wonderful for easing anger by giving a feeling of peace, love and tenderness.

Ylang Ylang is a feminine aroma that is uplifting and relaxing. It brings a sense of peace, re-uniting us with our emotional, caring, nurturing side, softening anger, and allowing us to feel safe. It balances the left and right brain: the logical and analytical with the emotional and intuitive. Ylang Ylang is the "warm fuzzy" emotionally nurturing essential oil.

When locked in that logical, analytical mode, use Ylang Ylang to relieve frustration. It softens us, bringing on an inner strength much stronger than any negative emotions we may show. Emotion is simply energy demanding motion.

ESSENTIAL OIL	EMOTIONAL BENEFITS
BASIL	SELF EXPRESSION
BERGAMOT	CHEERFULNESS
CEDARWOOD-VIRGINIAN	COURAGE
CHAMOMILE-GERMAN	LETTING GO
CINNAMON	COLDNESS AND INTROVERSION
CLARY SAGE	CLARITY
CLOVE BUD	REMOVES ATTACHMENTS
CYPRESS	TRANSITION
EUCALYPTUS	INTEGRATION
FENNEL-SWEET	ASSERTIVE / COMPLETION
FRANKINCENSE	PROTECTION
GERANIUM	REDUCES EXTREMES / RE-BALANCE
GINGER	STAMINA / PROCRASTINATION
GRAPEFRUIT	OPTIMISM
JASMINE	LIVE IN NOW WITH PASSION
JUNIPER	PREPARATION
LAVENDER	NURTURING
LEMON	RATIONALITY
LEMONGRASS	EXPANSION
LIME	EASES STRESS
MANDARIN	HAPPINESS
MARJORAM	ANXIETY
MAY CHANG	STIMULATING
MYRRH	INSPIRATION
NEROLI	CHOICES
NUTMEG	INCREASES ENERGY
ORANGE-SWEET	SERIOUSNESS
PALMAROSA	ADAPTABILITY
PATCHOULI	UNITY
PEPPER-BLACK	DIRECTION
PEPPERMINT	PURPOSE
PETITGRAIN	CONSCIOUS MIND
PINE	SELF WORTH
ROSE	LOVE
ROSEMARY	CREATIVITY
ROSEWOOD	RECEPTIVITY
SANDALWOOD	CONTEMPLATION
SPEARMINT	INVIGORATION
TEA TREE	UNDERSTANDING
THYME	WILLPOWER / STRENGTH
VETIVER	CENTRED
YLANG YLANG	PEACE

I have included a table of the physiological benefits of the essential oils. Although I have not expanded on the oils' talents, I have incorporated a brief overview for those who may wish to have this information.

The blending methods are the same as for the emotional uses of the essential oils, but use common sense. For instance, if you wanted to make up a blend for aches and pains, putting it in an oil burner will probably not relieve your pains. But if you blend the essential oils into a cold-pressed vegetable base and make a massage oil, you will get relief. Enjoy playing with this area of Aromatherapy.

PHYSIOLOGICAL BENEFITS

Basil	Memory and mental stimulant, nervous tension and exhaustion, brain and life overload.
Bergamot	Acne, uplifting, antidepressant, nervousness, cold sores, stimulates urinary system.
Cinnamon	Coughs, colds, antiseptic, warming, arthritis, aches and pains, nervous tension and exhaustion.
Cedarwood	Respiratory disorders, acne, astringent, antiseptic for skin, nervous tension, relaxant, grounding.
Clary Sage	Emotional stress, menstrual disorders, nervousness.
Clove	Analgesic, antiseptic, toothaches.
Cypress	Dysmenorrhoea, cellulite, varicose veins, uplifting, respiratory sedative, asthma.
Chamomile German	Anti inflammatory, sensitive skin, dermatitis, arthritis, nervous tension and stress, menstrual disorders, muscular pain.
Frankincense	Meditation, calming and grounding, antiseptic, astringent, expectorant, sedative.
Fennel	Diuretic, expectorant, relieves nausea and digestive disorders, stimulates estrogen, uplifting, tonifying, detoxifying.

Grapefruit	Astringent, cellulite, lymphatic system and gall bladder stimulant, Fluid retention, uplifts the spirit.
Geranium	Balances adrenals, moods and emotions. Dry and oily skin, nervous tension, sedative, uplifting, neuralgia.
Ginger	Warming, arthritis, muscular aches and pains, aids digestive system disorders, nervous exhaustion and tension, catarrh and colds.
Jasmine	Aphrodisiac, relaxing and emotionally soothing, irritated skin, aids in childbirth.
Juniper	Detoxifying, acne, dermatitis, cellulite, arthritis, invigorating, diuretic, amenorrhoea.
Lavender	Headaches, relaxing, cuts, scratches bump and bites, burns, antidepressant, suitable for all skin types.
Lemon	Bactericidal, infectious diseases, improves concentration, detoxifying, oily skin.
Lemongrass	Stimulating and uplifting, indigestion.
Lime	Stomach cramps, astringent, bronchitis, uplifting.
Mandarin	Aids digestion, calming and refreshing, relieves fluid retention, colic.
Marjoram	Insomnia, nervous tension, asthma, sedative.
May Chang	Cardiac tonic, antidepressant, invigorating but relaxing, hypertension.
Myrrh	Reduces inflammation, skin care, ulcers, uterine disorders, youthful complexion.
Neroli	Anti-depressant, insomnia, mood enhancing, uplifting, sedative.
Nutmeg	Aids digestion, warming, arthritis, relaxing, sensual.

Orange	Fun in a bottle, light-hearted, relaxing, nervousness, expels gas from the intestines.
Patchouli	Nerve stimulant, seductive, warm and fuzzy, rejuvenating, dry and mature skin.
Palmarosa	Acne, skin care, hydrating, refreshes moods and emotions.
Pine	Colds, flu, coughs, catarrh, sinus congestion, analgesic for muscular aches and pains.
Petitgrain	Invigorating, increases awareness, aids digestion.
Peppermint	Analgesic, digestive disorders, antiseptic, respiratory system, menstrual cramps, headaches.
Rose	Antidepressant, dry and mature skin, soothes heart emotions and relaxes, cooling and soothing on body systems.
Rosemary	Analgesic, arthritis, memory stimulant, mental fatigue, stimulant to liver and gall bladder.
Rosewood	Acne, relieves stress and anxiety, used extensively in skin care.
Sandalwood	Aphrodisiac, antidepressant, relaxant, bladder infections, sedative, dry and mature skin.
Tea Tree	Infections of all description, respiratory disorders, acne, cold sores, tinea.
Thyme	Bacterial and viral infections, respiratory disorders, mental exhaustion, stimulant.
Vetiver	Relaxing, grounding, reduces stress, used as a fixative.
Ylang Ylang	Aphrodisiac, sedative, soothes nerves and anger, antidepressant, mood enhancer.

Glossary

(The Big Words that you will find in Aromatherapy)

Abortifacient	An agent capable of inducing abortion.
Analgesic	Pain relieving.
Anaphrodisiac	Diminishing sexual desire.
Anti sudorophic	Reduces sweating.
Anti allergenic	Reduces allergy symptoms.
Anti arthritic	Reduces arthritic symptoms.
Anti emetic	Reduces incidence of severe vomiting.
Anti inflammatory	Relieves inflammation.
Anticonvulsive	Helps reduce or control convulsions.
Anti depressant	Counteracts melancholy, elevates moods.
Anti microbial	Destroys or resists pathogenic organisms.
Anti phlogistic	Reduces inflammation.
Anti puritic	Relieves or prevents itching.
Anti rheumatic	Relieves symptoms of rheumatism.
Antiseptic	Assists in the control of infection.
Antispasmodic	Relieves muscle spasm and cramps.
Aphrodisiac	Increases sexual desire.
Astringent	Contracts, tightens and binds tissues.
Bactericide	Bacteria destroying agent.
Cardiac	Stimulating effect on the heart.
Carminative	Expels gas and settles the digestive system.
Cephalic	Stimulates and clears the mind.
Cholagogue	Aids excretion and increases flow of bile into duodenum.
Cicatrisant	Assists in the formation of scar tissue.
Cordial	A tonic and stimulant for the heart.
Cytophylatic	Encourages the growth of skin cells.
Decongestant	Reduces congestion, e.g. nasal mucus.
Demulcent	Soothes and softens irritated mucous membranes.
Deodorant	Destroys odor.
Depurative	detoxifying, purifies the blood.
Diaphoretic	Promotes perspiration.
Digestive	Aids in the digestion of foods.

Disinfectant	Combats and prevents the spread of germs.
Diuretic	Increase the flow of urine.
Emetic	Induces vomiting.
Emmenagogue	Regulates and promotes menstrual flow.
Emollient	Soothes and softens skin.
Essential Oil	Natural oil extracted using distillation or expression.
Expectorant	Expels mucus from the respiratory system.
Febrifuge	Reduces body temperature and cools.
Fungicide	Destroys fungal infections.
Galactagogue	Increases milk secretion.
Germicidal	Destroys micro-organisms and germs.
Haemostatic	Arrests bleeding haemorrhage.
Hepatic	Stimulates function of liver and gall bladder.
Hypertensive	Increases blood pressure.
Hypotensive	Lowers blood pressure.
Insecticide	Repels insects.
Laxative	Aids bowel evacuation.
Mucolytic	Breaks down mucus.
Nervine	Strengthens and tones the nerves and nervous system.
Parturient	Assists in childbirth delivery.
Relaxant	Relieves tension and stress, soothes nerves.
Rubefacient	Warms and increases blood flow.
Sedative	Reduces functional activity, relaxes.
Soporofic	Induces sleep.
Splenetic	Spleen tonic.
Stimulant	Increases physiological functions of the body.
Stomachic	Improves appetite and digestive aid.
Styptic	Arrests external bleeding.
Sudorophic	Increases perspiration.
Tonic	Improves and strengthens body performance.
Uterine	Tones the uterus.
Vasoconstrictor	Contracts walls of blood vessels.
Vasodilator	Dilates walls of blood vessels.
Vermifuge	Expels worms.
Vulnerary	Arrests bleeding and prevents tissue damage.

Jennifer Jefferies

is available for seminars, conference addresses and organisational consulting.

Presentation topics include:

- √ **The Scentual Way to Success.**
- √ **Integrating Natural Therapies into your Organisation to Improve Health and Prevent Burn Out.**
- √ **How to Start Living and Stop Just Existing.**
- √ **The Emotional and Therapeutic Benefits of Aromatherapy.**
- √ **Regaining Responsibility and Your Passion in Life.**

For further information contact:

Jennifer Jefferies
Living Energy Natural Therapies
Shop 1, Shaws Arcade, Flinders Street Mall,
Townsville, Queensland 4810.
Australia.
Phone/Fax: 61 7 4721 3124
Email: email@livingenergy.com.au

How to Purchase the Essential Oils

All of the essential oils and associated products mentioned in this book are available for purchase from Living Energy Natural Therapies. For a complete set of catalogues and price list, post or fax the form below, or contact us on our web site at www.livingenergy.com.au

EASY FAX FORM

To: Living Energy Natural Therapies

Phone/Fax: 61 7 4721 3124

Please send me a FREE set of catalogues for your essential oils, additional Aromatherapy products and special corporate packages of Aromatherapy essential oils.

Name ______________________________

Postal Address ______________________________

______________________ Postcode ________

Phone Number ______________________________

Fax Number ______________________________

Email ______________________________

FAST FAX ORDER FORM

Phone/Fax: 07 4721 3124
Jennifer Jefferies
Living Energy Natural Therapies
Shop 1 Shaws Arcade, Flinders Street Mall.
Townsville, Q 4810, Australia.
Email: email@livingenergy.com.au

The following book and audio tape by Jennifer Jefferies are available for purchase. (Prices are quoted in Australian Dollars)

The Scentual Way to Success **$20**

Learning, the Aromatic way how to "Live and not just Exist."

Scentual Living (Audio Tape) **$35**

For those wanting to learn practical skills on how to regain responsibility and passion in their lives using Aromatherapy.

Please add $3.50 for postage and handling for a single item or $7.50 for two or more items, Express Post.

Name: ______________________________

Address: ______________________________

Phone: ______________ Fax: ______________

Email: ______________________________

Number of Books required ________ @ $20 - Cost $ __________

Number of Tapes required ________ @ $35 - Cost $ __________

Postage $ __________

Total Cost $ __________

Payment Method:

BANKCARD ☐ VISA ☐ MASTERCARD ☐

Name as on Credit Card ______________________________

Signature ______________________ Expiry Date __________

Credit Card Number: ☐☐☐☐ ☐☐☐☐ ☐☐☐☐ ☐☐☐☐

I enclose cheque for $ ______________

Please make cheques payable to Jennifer Jefferies

Quantity Orders Invited

For Bulk Discounts Contact Jennifer

Suggested Reading

Some other great titles for you to enjoy

The Complete Guide to Aromatherapy by Salvatore Battaglia

Be Seen, Get Known, Move Ahead by Robyn Henderson

Are You the VIP in Your Life? by Robyn Henderson

How to Master Networking by Robyn Henderson

Networking Magic by Robyn Henderson

You Can Heal Your Life by Louise L. Hay

Your Body is the Barometer of Your Soul by Annette Noontil

Love your Disease by Dr John Harrison

Anatomy of Illness by Norman Cousins

Clicking by Faith Popcorn

Aromatherapy for Healing The Spirit by Gabriel Mojay

The Fragrant Pharmacy by Valerie Ann Worwood

Australian Bush Flower Essences by Ian White

Succulent Wild Woman by SARK

Aromatherapy Scent and Psyche by P & K Damian

Aromatherapy and the Mind by Julia Lawless

Portraits in Oils by P. Mailhebbiau

Thick Face Black Heart by Chin-Ning Chu

Inspirational Sandwich by SARK

A Creative Companion by SARK

Bibliography

Battaglia, S. *The Complete Guide to Aromatherapy.*
The Perfect Potion, Australia, (1995).

Damian, P&K. *Aromatherapy Scent and Psyche.*
Healing Arts Press. Canada (1995)

Fischer-Rizzi, S. *Complete Aromatherapy Handbook.*
Sterling, London. (1990)

Lawless, J. *Aromatherapy and the Mind.*
Harper Collins, London. (1994)

Mailhebbiau, P. *Portraits in Oils.*
C.W. Daniel Company, Great Britain (1995)

Mojay, G. *Aromatherapy for Healing The Spirit.*
Hodder & Stoughton, Australia. (1996)

Worwood, V.A. *The Fragrant Mind.*
Transworld, Australia. (1995)

Zeck, R. *Aromatic Kinesiology.*
R.Zeck, Australia (1996)

References

(1) Tisserand, R. Lemon Fragrance Increases Office Efficiency. International Journal of Aromatherapy Vol 1, No.2 (1988) p.2.

(2) Ryman, D. The Aromatherapy Handbook. Century, (1984) p.85.

(3) Davis, P. Subtle Aromatherapy. C.W. Daniel, (1991) p.203.

(4) Lovell, R. A compleat Herball, 2nd Edition, (1665) p.436.

Index